The Montana Council of Teachers of Mathematics

The Systemic Initiative for Montana Mathematics and Science

INTEGRATED MATHEMATICS

A MODELING APPROACH USING TECHNOLOGY

TEACHER'S EDITION

Level **2**

Volume **2**

SIMON & SCHUSTER CUSTOM PUBLISHING

SIMMS PROJECT CO-DIRECTORS

Johnny W. Lott • Maurice Burke

MATERIALS DEVELOPMENT COMMITTEE

Dean Preble • Terry Souhrada

ASSESSMENT COMMITTEE

James Hirstein • Sharon Walen

PROFESSIONAL DEVELOPMENT COMMITTEE

Glenn Allinger • Michael Lundin

TECHNICAL EDITOR

Peter Fong

SIMMS CURRICULUM REVIEWERS

Participants of the SIMMS Teacher Institutes and Staff

This material is based upon work supported by the National Science
Foundation under Cooperative Agreement No. OSR 9150055 and ESI–9616267. Any opinions,
findings, conclusions or recommendations expressed in this material are those
of the author(s) and do not necessarily reflect the views of the
National Science Foundation.

Printed in the United States of America.

10 9 8 7 6 5 4 3 2

BA 98272

ISBN 0–536–59533-X

SIMON & SCHUSTER CUSTOM PUBLISHING
160 Gould Street/Needham Heights, MA 02194
Simon & Schuster Education Group

About SIMMS Integrated Mathematics

The Need for Change

In recent years, many voices have called for the reform of mathematics education in the United States. Teachers, scholars, and administrators alike have pointed out the symptoms of a flawed system. From the ninth grade onwards, for example, about half of the students in this country's mathematical pipeline are lost each year (National Research Council, 1990, p. 36). Attempts to identify the root causes of this decline have targeted not only the methods used to instruct and assess our students, but the nature of the mathematics they learn and the manner in which they are expected to learn. In its *Curriculum and Evaluation Standards for School Mathematics*, the National Council of Teachers of Mathematics addressed the problem in these terms:

> Deciding on the content of school mathematics is the initial step in the necessary change process. . . .
> We now challenge educators to integrate mathematics topics across courses so that students can view major mathematical ideas from more than one perspective and bring interrelated ideas to bear on new topics or problems. . . .
> We favor . . . a truly integrated curricular organization in all grades to permit students to develop mathematical power more readily and to allow the necessary flexibility over time to incorporate the content of these standards. (p. 251–52)

Some Methods for Change

The Systemic Initiative for Montana Mathematics and Science (SIMMS) was a five-year, cooperative initiative of the state of Montana and the National Science Foundation. Funded through the Montana Council of Teachers of Mathematics, the SIMMS Project included the following among its major objectives:

- the redesign of the 9–12 mathematics curriculum using an integrated inter-disciplinary approach for *all* students.
- the incorporation of the use of technology in all facets and at all levels of mathematics and science.
- the development of curriculum and assessment materials for grades 9–16.

The SIMMS Curriculum

An integrated mathematics program "consists of topics chosen from a wide variety of mathematical fields. . . [It] emphasizes the relationships among topics within mathematics as well as between mathematics and other disciplines" (Beal, et al., 1992; Lott, 1991). In order to create innovative, integrated, and accessible materials, the SIMMS curriculum was written, revised, and reviewed by secondary teachers of mathematics and science. SIMMS materials encourage participation by women and members of ethnic minorities, and are intended for use by heterogeneous groupings of students. They are designed to replace all currently offered secondary mathematics courses, with the possible exception of Advanced Placement Calculus, and build on middle-school reform initiatives, such as the Six Through Eight Mathematics (STEM) Project.

SIMMS curricular materials are partitioned into six levels. All students should take at least the first two levels. In the third and fourth years, SIMMS offers a choice of options, depending on student interests and goals. A flow chart of the curriculum appears in Figure 1.

Entry Point

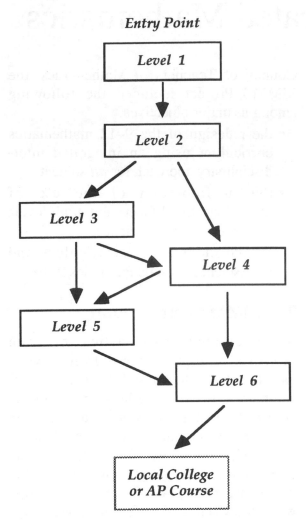

Figure 1: SIMMS course sequence

Each year-long level contains 14–16 modules. Some must be presented in sequence, while others may be studied in any order. Modules are further divided into several activities, typically including an exploration, a discussion, a set of homework assignments, and a research project.

Assessment materials—including alternative assessments that emphasize writing and logical argument—are an integral part of the curriculum. Suggested assessment items for use with a standard rubric are identified in all teacher editions. Each module also contains an open-ended, often project-oriented summary assessment, as well as a more traditional assessment (for use at the teacher's discretion).

Level 1: a first-year course for ninth graders (or possibly eighth graders)

Level 1 concentrates on the knowledge and understanding that students need to become mathematically literate citizens, while providing the necessary foundation for those who wish to pursue careers involving mathematics and science. Contexts for the presentation of mathematics include the properties of reflected light, population growth, the AIDS epidemic, and the manufacture of cardboard containers. Mathematical content includes data collection, presentation, and interpretation; introductions to linear, exponential, and step equations; and three-dimensional geometry, including surface area and volume.

Level 2: a second-year course for either ninth or tenth graders

Level 2 continues to build on the mathematics that students need to become mathematically literate citizens. While retaining an emphasis on the presentation and interpretation of data, Level 2 introduces trigonometric ratios and matrices, while also encouraging the development of algebraic skills. Contexts include pyramid construction, small business inventory, genetics, and the allotment of seats in the U.S. House of Representatives.

Levels 3 and 4: options for students in their third year in SIMMS

Both of these levels build on the mathematics content in Level 2 and provide an opportunity for students to expand their mathematical understanding. While most students planning careers in mathematics and science will choose Level 4, Level 3 also provides insight into some topics typically studied by mathematics and science majors.

Contexts in Level 4 include launching a new business, historic rainfall patterns, topography, and scheduling. The mathematical content includes rational, logarithmic, and circular functions, proofs, and combinatorics.

In Level 3, module contexts include nutrition, surveying, and quality control. Mathematical topics include linear programming, polynomial functions, and curve fitting.

Levels 5 and 6: options for students in their fourth year in SIMMS

Level 6 materials continue the presentation of mathematics through applied contexts while embracing a broader mathematical perspective. For example, Level 6 modules explore operations on functions, instantaneous rates of change, complex numbers, and parametric equations.

Level 5 focuses more specifically on applications from business and the social sciences, including statistics testing, logic circuits, and game theory.

More About Level 2

"Marvelous Matrices" introduces matrix operations in the context of business inventories. "When to Deviate from a Mean Task" and "And the Survey Says . . ." focus on statistics and sampling, respectively. "A New Angle on an Old Pyramid," "There's No Place Like Home," and "Crazy Cartoons" have primarily geometric themes. "Traditional Design" also explores some geometric topics—this time from the perspective of American Indian star quilts. "Who Gets What and Why?" examines the mathematics of apportionment to the U.S. House of Representatives. Other modules explore linear programming, multistage probability, models of exponential decay, curve fitting, and the limits of sequences and series. Some teachers may wish to schedule the genetics module—"What Are My Child's Chances?"—in coordination with a biology class.

The Teacher Edition

To facilitate use of the curriculum, the teacher edition contains these features:

Overview /Objectives/Prerequisites

Each module begins with a brief overview of its contents. This overview is followed by a list of teaching objectives and a list of prerequisite skills and knowledge.

Time Line/Materials & Technology Required

A time line provides a rough estimate of the classroom periods required to complete each module. The materials required for the entire module are listed by activity. The technology required to complete the module appears in a similar list.

Assignment Problems/Assessment Items/Flashbacks

Assignment problems appear at the end of each activity. These problems are separated into two sections by a series of asterisks. The problems in the first section cover all the essential elements in the activity. The second section provides optional problems for extra practice or additional homework.

Specific assignment problems recommended for assessment are preceded by a single asterisk in the teacher edition. Each module also contains a Summary Assessment in the student edition and a Module Assessment in the teacher edition, for use at the teacher's discretion. In general, Summary Assessments offer more open-ended questions, while Module Assessments take a more traditional approach.

To review prerequisite skills, each module includes brief problem sets called "Flashbacks." Like the Module Assessment, they are designed for use at the teacher's discretion.

Technology in the Classroom

The SIMMS curriculum requires the appropriate use of technology. Individual graphing calculators should be available to all students. Classroom technology should have the functionality and memory to run a word processing program, a statistics package, a graphing package, a symbolic manipulator, a spreadsheet program, and a geometric drawing utility. In addition, SIMMS students should have access to a telephone modem, as well as a science interface device that allows for electronic data collection from classroom experiments.

In the student edition, references to technology provide as much flexibility as possible to the teacher. In the teacher edition, sample responses refer to specific pieces of technology, where applicable.

Professional Development

A program of professional development is recommended for all teachers planning to use the SIMMS curriculum. SIMMS materials encourage the use of cooperative learning, consider mathematical topics in a different order than in a traditional curriculum, and teach some mathematical topics not previously encountered at the high-school level. Teachers must also learn to use alternative assessments, to integrate writing and communication into the mathematics curriculum, and to help students incorporate technology in their own investigations of mathematical ideas.

Approximately 100 classroom teachers and 15 university professors are available to present inservice workshops for interested school districts. Please contact Simon & Schuster Custom Publishing for more information.

Project Assessment to Date

Assessment instruments have been administered in selected SIMMS classes using Levels 1–6. On both the non-technology-based PSAT and a test of problem-solving skills allowing use of technology, the results are very encouraging. When compared with the control group, students in SIMMS classes did as well as students in a traditional program on a test of general mathematical knowledge. On more open-ended questions, SIMMS students showed superior skills in problem-solving and communicating mathematical ideas, used a wider variety of problem-solving strategies, and used appropriate technology.

References

Beal, J., D. Dolan, J. Lott, and J. Smith. *Integrated Mathematics: Definitions, Issues, and Implications; Report and Executive Summary.* ERIC Clearinghouse for Science, Mathematics, and Environmental Education. The Ohio State University, Columbus, OH: ED 347071, January 1990, 115 pp.

Lott, J., and A. Reeves. "The Integrated Mathematics Project," *Mathematics Teacher* 84 (April 1991): 334–35.

National Council of Teachers of Mathematics (NCTM). *Curriculum and Evaluation Standards for School Mathematics.* Reston, VA: NCTM, 1989.

National Research Council. *A Challenge of Numbers: People in the Mathematical Sciences.* Washington, DC: National Academy Press, 1990.

The SIMMS Project. *Monograph 1: Philosophies.* Missoula, MT: The Montana Council of Teachers of Mathematics, 1993.

Contents

There's No Place Like Home

What geometric shape does your home resemble? What do you think the houses of the future will look like? In this module, you explore some traditional American Indian housing designs—from the ground up.

Kyle Boyce • *Clay Burkett*

There's No Place Like Home

Overview

In this module, students use traditional American Indian housing designs to investigate the surface areas and volumes of some common three-dimensional figures. An intuitive understanding of limits is developed by exploring a circle as the limit of a progression of regular polygons with an increasing number of sides inscribed in the circle. Similarly, a cylinder is presented as the limit of a progression of regular polygonal right prisms inscribed in the cylinder, and a cone as the limit of a progression of regular pyramids inscribed in the cone. Students also explore the ratio of surface area to volume as a measure of structural efficiency.

Objectives

In this module, students will:

- determine the areas of regular polygons and circles

- determine the surface areas and volumes of prisms, pyramids, cylinders, and cones

- calculate the surface areas and volumes of spheres

- identify a circle as the limiting shape for its inscribed regular polygons, a cylinder as the limiting shape for its inscribed regular prisms, and a cone as the limiting shape for its inscribed regular pyramids.

Prerequisites

For this module, students should know:

- how to use the sine, cosine, and tangent ratios to determine unknown lengths and angle measures in right triangles

- how to calculate the perimeter of a regular polygon given the length of a side

- how to express the area of a regular polygon as the sum of the areas of congruent isosceles triangles with their vertex angle at the center of the polygon

- how to calculate the circumference and area of a circle

- the parts of a prism

- how to determine the volume of a prism

- how to make nets of three-dimensional figures

- the Pythagorean theorem.

Time Line

Activity	1	2	3	4	5	Summary Assessment	Total
Days	1	1	2	2	2	1	9

Materials Required

Materials	Activity					
	1	2	3	4	5	Summary Assessment
construction paper				X	X	
scissors				X	X	
tape				X	X	
cubes			X			
compass					X	
ruler					X	
rice					X	

Technology

Materials	Activity					
	1	2	3	4	5	Summary Assessment
geometry utility	X			X	X	
graphing utility					X	
spreadsheet	X				X	

There's No Place Like Home

Introduction (page 149)

This module uses traditional American Indian housing designs as a context for studying the surface areas and volumes of prisms, cylinders, pyramids, cones, and spheres.

(page 149)

Activity 1

In this activity, students explore the areas of regular polygons. This provides the basis for determining surface area throughout the module. The idea of a circle as the limit of a progression of its inscribed regular polygons is introduced here.

Materials List

- none

Technology

- geometry utility
- spreadsheet (optional)

Teacher Note

Since the following exploration can be time consuming, you may wish to divide the polygons in Part **c** among several groups, then ask students to compile their results. (If so, all students should use the same radius when constructing the inscribed polygons.)

Exploration (page 149)

a–b.   Students use a geometry utility to draw an inscribed regular triangle, then determine its perimeter and area.

c–d.   The following sample data was collected using a radius of 5 cm.

Regular Polygon	Perimeter (cm)	Area (cm²)
triangle	26.0	32.4
square	28.3	49.9
pentagon	29.4	59.3
hexagon	30.0	64.8
octagon	30.6	70.6
18-gon	31.2	76.8
circle	31.4	78.4

Discussion

(page 150)

a. Sample response: The number of sides in the polygon equals its number of central angles. Since there are 360° in a circle, 360° divided by the number of sides (or vertices) determines how many degrees each central angle must have. To find the vertices, locate the points on the circle where each central angle has the desired measure.

b. The congruent central angles form congruent isosceles triangles in each polygon, with the base of each triangle representing a side of the polygon. Since the bases of these triangles are all congruent, the sides of the polygon are congruent. Since the base angles of all the isosceles triangles are congruent, the angles of the polygon are congruent.

c. **1.** One method divides the regular polygon into congruent isosceles triangles with vertex angles at the center of the polygon and bases as the sides of the polygon. The area of each of these triangles, where a is the height and b is the length of the base, is

$$\frac{1}{2}ab$$

The area of the polygon is equal to the sum of the areas of these triangles. If the polygon has n sides, then the area of the polygon is

$$n\left(\frac{1}{2}ab\right)$$

Since $n \cdot b$ is the perimeter of the polygon, the generalized form of this method is the formula

$$A = \frac{1}{2}ap$$

where a is the apothem and p is the perimeter. **Note:** Students also may suggest using technology, as described in the exploration.

2. Sample response: Each method can be useful, depending on the information given. Using a formula is appropriate when you know the required lengths. Using technology can be faster if you have already drawn a model of the polygon.

d. **1.** The shape of the polygon approaches a circle.

2. The area of the polygon approaches the area of the circle.

3. The perimeter of the polygon approaches the circumference of the circle.

e. **1.** The shape of the polygon approaches a circle.

2. The area of the polygon approaches the area of the circle.

3. The perimeter of the polygon approaches the circumference of the circle.

192

f.   **1.**   Sample response: As the number of sides of the polygon increases, the shape of the polygon becomes more and more circular. The apothem approaches a radius (r) of the circle and the perimeter approaches the circumference ($2\pi r$) of the circle.

2.   As the number of sides increases, the formula for the area of a regular polygon approaches the formula for the area of a circle:

$$A = \frac{1}{2}r(2\pi r) = \pi r^2$$

Assignment   (page 153)

1.1   **a.** $m\angle ABC = 20°$; $m\angle ABD = 10°$

b. $AD = (\sin 10°)/5 \approx 0.87$ m

c. $AC \approx 1.74$ m

d.   Using the Pythagorean theorem, $BD \approx 4.9$ m.

e.   The area of $\triangle ABC \approx (4.9 \cdot 1.74)/2 \approx 4.3$ m^2.

f.   The area of the floor is approximately $18(4.3) \approx 77$ m^2.

*1.2   Student methods may vary. Using the points labeled in the diagram below, $AB = 8$ m, $\sin 67.5° = BD/8$, and $\cos 67.5° = AD/8$.

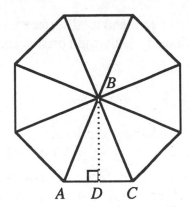

The area of the floor, therefore, can be found as follows:

$$A = \frac{1}{2}a \cdot p$$

$$= \frac{1}{2}(8 \cdot \sin 67.5°) \cdot 2(8 \cdot \cos 67.5°)8 \approx 181 \text{ m}^2$$

1.3   Using the formula for the area of a circle, the area of the floor is $\pi(3.5/2)^2 \approx 9.6$ m^2.

* * * * *

1.4   Student methods may vary. Using the formula for the area of a regular polygon, the area of the floor is:

$$A = \frac{1}{2} a \cdot p$$

$$= \frac{1}{2}(0.5\sqrt{3} \cdot 6) \approx 2.6 \text{ m}^2$$

* * * * * * * * * *

Research Project   (page 154)

This research project gives students the opportunity to further explore the geometric and cultural aspects of traditional American Indian housing designs. You may wish to encourage students to build models or make sketches.

(page 154)

Activity 2

Students examine lateral surface area and total surface area using nets of right prisms and right circular cylinders. (Only right prisms and cylinders are considered in the context of this module.)

Materials List
- none

Technology
- geometry utility (optional)

Discussion   (page 155)

a.   **1.** Sample response: The bases of a prism must be parallel. Since the rectangles are not parallel, the floor cannot be a base.

   2. Sample response: It is called a right prism because the bases are perpendicular to the lateral faces.

b.   The length of $\overline{AD}$ (or $\overline{BC}$) equals the perimeter of the base.

194

c. Sample response: Determine the area of a base by squaring the length of one side of the base. Find the area of the lateral surface by multiplying the perimeter of the base by the height of the prism. Add the area of the two bases to the area of the lateral surface.

d.
1. The length of the rectangle's longer side is the circumference of the cylinder.

2. The length of the rectangle's shorter side is the height of the cylinder.

3. The circles represent the two bases of the cylinder.

4. The length of the rectangle's longer side is $2\pi r$

5. Sample response: Multiply the circumference of the cylinder by the height to find the lateral surface area. Find the area of a base by squaring the radius and then multiplying by π. Add the lateral surface area to two times the area of a base.

Assignment

(page 156)

2.1 a–b. Sample response:

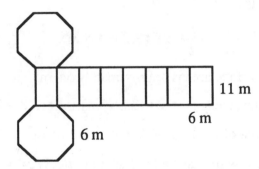

11 m

6 m

6 m

c. The lateral surface area is $8 \bullet 6 \bullet 11 = 528$ m^2.

d. Sample response:

$$A = 2 \bullet n \left(\frac{1}{2} ab \right)$$

$$= 2 \bullet 8 \left(\frac{1}{2} \bullet 6 \bullet \frac{3}{\tan 22.5°} \right)$$

$$\approx 348 \text{ m}^2$$

e. The total surface area is $528 + 348 = 876$ m^2.

2.2   **a.** Sample sketch:

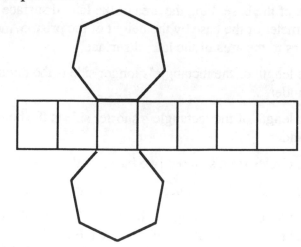

   b. Sample response: As the number of sides increases, the base gets closer and closer to a circle. The shape of the prism approaches a cylinder.

2.3   The lateral surface area, including the floor, is $3 \bullet 3.2 \bullet 4.7 \approx 45 \text{ m}^2$. The height of the triangular base is $1.6 \bullet \tan 60° \approx 2.8 \text{ m}$. The area of each base is

$$\frac{1}{2} \bullet 2.8 \bullet 3.2 \approx 4.5 \text{ m}^2$$

The total surface area is approximately 54 m^2.

2.4   The total surface area is $2 \bullet (3.8 \bullet 3.4) + 2 \bullet (3.8 + 3.4) \bullet 2.2 = 57.5 \text{ m}^2$.

*2.5   **a.** The area of the floor is $3.7 \bullet 4.9 \approx 18.1 \text{ m}^2$.

   b. The two walls have a total area of $\pi(3.7/2)^2 \approx 10.8 \text{ m}^2$.

   c. The lateral surface area can be found as follows:

$$\frac{1}{2} \bullet 2\pi(3.7/2) \bullet 4.9 \approx 28.5 \text{ m}^2$$

   d. The total surface area is $18.1 + 28.5 + 10.8 \approx 57.4 \text{ m}^2$.

* * * * *

2.6   Sample response: The amount of bark required to cover the Iroquois house (not including the floor) is the area of the four walls plus the area of the half cylinder that represents the roof:

$$2(5.5 + 18.3) \bullet 2.75 + \pi(2.75)^2 + \frac{1}{2}(2\pi \bullet 2.75) \bullet 18.3 \approx 313 \text{ m}^2$$

* * * * * * * * *

Activity 3

Students compare the volumes of various American Indian structures. They also consider the ratio of surface area to volume as a measure of a building's heating (or cooling) efficiency.

Materials List

- sets of eight cubes (one or two sets per group)

Exploration

(page 159)

In this exploration, students investigate the relationship between volume and surface area.

a–b. Students should record each arrangement of the cubes they investigate.

c. In general, the total surface area depends on the number of faces shared by the cubes. The diagram below shows a top view of three sample arrangements with a surface area of $34\ \text{units}^2$.

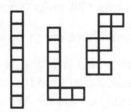

The following diagram shows the top view of six additional arrangements of cubes.

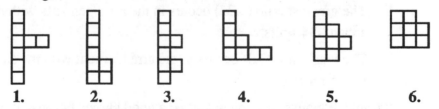

1.   2.   3.   4.   5.   6.

The diagram below shows several arrangements in which the cubes are stacked.

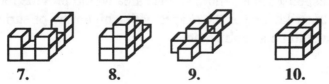

7.   8.   9.   10.

The total surface area and ratio of surface area to volume for each arrangement are shown in the table below.

Arrangement	Surface Area (units^2)	Surface Area / Volume
1	34	4.25
2	32	4
3	34	4.25
4	32	4
5	30	3.75
6	28	3.5
7	34	4.25
8	30	3.75
9	34	4.25
10	24	3

Discussion

(page 159)

a.
1. The greatest surface area (34 units^2) occurs in several different arrangements.

2. The least surface area (24 units^2) occurs in a $2 \times 2 \times 2$ arrangement.

3. All the arrangements have the same volume, 8 units^3.

b. Sample response: Given that two designs have the same volume, a design with more surface area (and therefore a higher ratio) would be more in contact with the outside air. While it might receive more sunlight during the day, it would also lose more heat whenever the outside air was colder than the inside air.

c.
1. The greatest ratio (4.25) occurs in the arrangements with the surface area of 34 units^2.

2. The least ratio (3.0) occurs in the arrangement with the surface area of 24 units^2.

d. Sample response: A cube would be a good choice because it has the smallest surface area for a given volume.

e. Sample response: Since more surface area would provide more area for sunlight to strike, one of the shapes with a high ratio of surface area to volume would be a good choice.

Assignment

3.1 **a.** The volume inside a Mohave-type house ranges from $6^2 \cdot 2.2 \approx 79.2 \text{ m}^3$ to about $7.5^2 \cdot 2.2 \approx 124 \text{ m}^3$.

  b. The ratio of surface area to volume is:

$$\frac{2(6 \cdot 6) + 4(2.2 \cdot 6)}{79.2} \approx 1.58$$

3.2 **a.** The ratio of surface area to volume is:

$$\frac{2(4 \cdot 3.25 + 2.2 \cdot 3.25 + 2.2 \cdot 4)}{2.2(4)3.25} \approx 2.02$$

  b. The volume of the Pueblo dwelling is about $13 \cdot 2.2 \approx 29 \text{ m}^3$. This is about 50 m^3 less space than the smallest Yuma dwelling.

3.3 **a.** The volume of the house is:

$$(4.1 \cdot 3.1 \cdot 1.7) + \left(\frac{3.1 \cdot 1}{2} \cdot 4.1\right) \approx 28 \text{ m}^3$$

  b. The surface area of the house is:

$$4.1 \cdot 3.1 + 2(1.7 \cdot 3.1 + 1.7 \cdot 4.1) + 2\left(\frac{3.1 \cdot 1}{2}\right) + 2(1.84 \cdot 4.1) \approx 55 \text{ m}^2$$

The ratio of surface area to volume is $55/28 \approx 1.96$.

*3.4 **a.** Because the floors and side walls are the same sizes, students need only compare those portions of the structures that lie above the side walls. The surface area of this portion of the building with the curved roof is:

$$\frac{2 \cdot \pi \cdot 1.5 \cdot 3.8}{2} + \pi \cdot (1.5)^2 \approx 25 \text{ m}^2$$

The surface area of this portion of the other structure is:

$$2 \cdot \left(\frac{1.5 \cdot 3.0}{2}\right) + 2(1.5\sqrt{2} \cdot 3.8) \approx 21 \text{ m}^2$$

Therefore, the surface area of the building with the curved roof is about 4 m^2 greater than that of the other building.

b. The volume of the portion of the building with the curved roof that lies above the side walls is:

$$\frac{\pi \cdot 1.5^2 \cdot 3.8}{2} \approx 13.4 \text{ m}^3$$

The volume of the corresponding portion of the other building is:

$$\frac{3.0 \cdot 1.5}{2} \cdot 3.8 \approx 8.6 \text{ m}^3$$

Therefore, the volume of the building with the curved roof is about 5 m^3 greater than that of the other building.

c. Sample response: Because heat is lost through surface area, you might expect the building with the curved roof to lose heat more easily. But this structure also has more volume. In fact, the ratio of surface area to volume for the building with the curved roof is $25/13.4 \approx 1.9$, while the ratio for the other building is $21/8.6 \approx 2.4$. Judging from these ratios, the building with the curved roof is likely to be more efficient in retaining heat.

3.5 **a.** Sample response: As the number of sides increases, the volume of the prism approaches the volume of the cylinder.

b. 1. Sample response: Yes, the formula can also be used to find the volume of a cylinder. You just need to find the area of the circular base and multiply it by the height of the cylinder.

2. Since the base of a cylinder is a circle, the formula for its area is $A = \pi r^2$.

* * * * *

3.6 **a.** The lateral surface area of the cylindrical container is about 1040 cm^2. The total surface area is approximately 1480 cm^2. The volume is approximately 4360 cm^3.

b. The lateral surface area of the container shaped like a rectangular prism is about 1280 cm^2. The total surface area is approximately 1620 cm^2. The volume is approximately 4020 cm^3.

c. Sample response: Since the cylindrical container has less surface area, it should take less material to manufacture each one. Therefore, it should be cheaper to produce.

* * * * * * * * * *

Activity 4

Students examine the surface area and volume of both pyramids and cones. Using nets, they also explore the notion of a cone as the limit of a progression of regular polygonal pyramids with the same heights whose bases are inscribed in the same circle.

Materials List

- construction paper (one sheet per student)
- tape
- scissors

Technology

- geometry utility (optional)

Discussion 1   (page 163)

a. The lateral faces are congruent isosceles triangles.

b. 1. The shape of the base becomes more and more circular.

2. The lengths of the bases of the congruent isosceles triangles decrease.

3. The pyramid looks more like a cone.

c. Sample response: To find the surface area of a pyramid, find the area of the polygonal base and the area of all the lateral triangular faces. Add the area of the base to the area of all the triangles.

Exploration   (page 163)

a. 1. Sample net:

2. Students should fold the net into a pyramid.

201

b. **1–2.** The following diagram shows a sample net of the lateral surface (with tape):

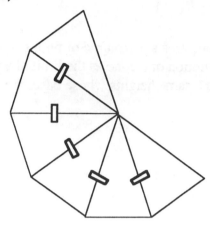

Discussion 2

(page 164)

a.   **1.** Sample response: The shape of the net looks like a concave polygon.

  2. Sample response: As the number of faces increases, the net of the lateral surface would look more like a part of a circle.

b.   **1.** The quantity $2\pi(10)$ represents the circumference of the circle.

  2. The ratio 40/360 represents the fraction of the circle represented by the shaded sector in Figure **9**.

c.   The quantity $\pi(10)^2$ represents the area of the circle.

d.   As the number of faces increases, the net of the lateral surface approaches a sector of a circle.

e.   **1.** The radius of the sector determines the slant height of the cone.

  2. The arc length of the sector determines the circumference of the cone's base.

  3. Sample response: Find the arc length of the sector. This is the circumference of the base of the cone. Since the circumference is $2\pi r$, you can then solve for the radius of the base of the cone.

Assignment

(page 165)

4.1   To find the area of the base, students must determine the apothem of the hexagon, $3\sqrt{3}$ m. To find the area of each triangular face, they must determine the slant height of the pyramid, $\sqrt{43}$ m. The total surface area can be found as follows:

$$6\left(\frac{6 \cdot 3\sqrt{3}}{2}\right) + 6\left(\frac{\sqrt{43} \cdot 6}{2}\right) \approx 212 \text{ m}^2$$

4.2   **a.** **1.** $\pi(5)^2 \approx 78.5$ cm^2

   2. $2\pi \cdot 5 \approx 31.4$ cm

b. **1.** The fraction of the circle represented by each unshaded sector is shown below:

$$\frac{270°}{360°} = \frac{3}{4}, \ \frac{240°}{360°} = \frac{2}{3}, \ \frac{300°}{360°} = \frac{5}{6}$$

   2. The areas of these unshaded sectors are:

$$\frac{3}{4}\pi(5)^2 \approx 58.9 \text{ cm}^2, \ \frac{2}{3}\pi(5)^2 \approx 52.4 \text{ cm}^2, \ \frac{5}{6}\pi(5)^2 \approx 65.4 \text{ cm}^2$$

   3. The corresponding arc lengths are:

$$\frac{3}{4}(2\pi)5 \approx 23.6 \text{ cm}, \ \frac{2}{3}(2\pi)5 \approx 20.9 \text{ cm}, \ \frac{5}{6}(2\pi)5 \approx 26.2 \text{ cm}$$

c. **1.** The arc length of the sector is the circumference of the base of the cone.

   2. From Part **b3**, the circumference of the base of this cone is 23.6 cm. The radius of the base, therefore, is $r = 23.6/2\pi \approx 3.8$ cm. The slant height of the cone is the radius of the original circle, 5 cm. Using the Pythagorean theorem, the height of the cone can be found as follows:

$$3.8^2 + h^2 = 5^2$$
$$h = 3.2 \text{ cm}$$

   3. The area of the base of the cone is $\pi \cdot 3.8^2 \approx 45.4$ cm^2.

   4. The total surface area is:

$$\frac{270}{360} \cdot \pi(5)^2 + \pi(3.8)^2 \approx 104.3 \text{ cm}^2$$

*4.3   **a.** Sample sketch:

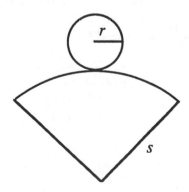

203

b. **1.** $2\pi r$

   2. $2\pi s$

   3. By comparing the length of the arc of the curved part of the net with the circumference of the large circle, the fraction of the large circle represented by the cone's lateral surface is:

$$\frac{2\pi r}{2\pi s} = \frac{r}{s}$$

c. **1.** πs^2

   2. The area of the lateral surface of the cone is:

$$\frac{r}{s}\left(\pi s^2\right) = \pi rs$$

d. Sample response: The total surface area is the sum of the lateral surface area and the area of the base: $A = \pi r^2 + \pi rs$.

e. Using the Pythagorean theorem, $h = \sqrt{s^2 - r^2}$.

4.4 **a.** The circumference of the floor is determined by the length of the semicircular arc, $\pi(2.5)$ m. Thus, the diameter of the floor is 2.5 m.

   b. Since the radius of the floor is 1.25 m and the slant height of the tipi is 2.5 m, $h = \sqrt{2.5^2 - 1.25^2} \approx 2.2$ m.

   c. Sample response: This is a very small tipi. A person could only stand up in the center, and it could sleep no more than two people.

* * * * *

4.5 **a.** In order to determine the radius of the template, students must first recognize that the central angle which defines each funnel, including the tab, measures 120°. Since the central angle for the tab measures 10°, the fraction of the circle that actual forms the funnel is 110°/360°.

   Since the length of the arc that forms the larger opening of the funnel is 32 cm, the radius of the circle can be found as follows:

$$\frac{110°}{360°} \bullet 2\pi r = 32$$

$$r = \frac{32}{2\pi} \bullet \frac{360°}{110°}$$

$$r \approx 16.7 \text{ cm}$$

b. Similarly, the radius of the inner circle can be determined as shown:

$$\frac{110°}{360°} \cdot 2\pi r = 5$$

$$r = \frac{5}{2\pi} \cdot \frac{360°}{110°}$$

$$r \approx 2.6 \text{ cm}$$

c. Students should recognize that the height of the funnel is the difference between the height of the cone before the tip is cut off and the height of the small cone which forms the tip.

The slant height of the larger cone is the radius of the larger circle, 16.7 cm. Since the radius of its base is approximately 5.1 cm, its height is $\sqrt{16.7^2 - 5.1^2} \approx 15.9$ cm.

The slant height of the smaller cone (the tip) is the radius of the inner circle, 2.6 cm. Since the radius of its base is approximately 0.8 cm, its height is $\sqrt{2.6^2 - 0.8^2} \approx 2.5$ cm.

The height of the funnel is $15.9 - 2.5 = 13.4$ cm.

* * * * * * * * * *

(page 168)

Activity 5

In this activity, students explore cones created from sectors of a circle. They also examine volume, surface area, and the ratio of surface area to volume for various cones and spheres.

Materials List

- compass (one per group)
- scissors (one pair per group)
- construction paper (four sheets per group)
- ruler (one per group)
- tape
- rice (about 2 cups per group)

Technology

- geometry utility
- spreadsheet

Exploration 1 (page 168)

Students examine cones made from sectors of a circle with a fixed radius.

a. Students draw a circle, cut it along a radius, and form a cone by overlapping the edges and taping the overlapped edge.

b. Students measure the height and radius of their cone.

c. Students create the lateral surface of a right circular cylinder with the same base and height as their cone. They form a cylinder by taping the edges together at the tab.

d. The ratio of the volume of the cylinder to that of the cone should be 3/1. Student results may vary slightly due to measuring and construction errors.

Discussion 1 (page 169)

a. The volume of the cylinder is three times the volume of a cone with the same base and height.

b. The formula for the volume of a right circular cylinder with radius r and height h is $V = \pi r^2 h$. It follows that the volume of a right circular cone with radius r and height h is

$$V = \frac{1}{3}\pi r^2 h$$

Exploration 2 (page 169)

Students investigate the relationship between the volume of a right prism and the volume of a regular pyramid with the same base and height.

a. Sample net:

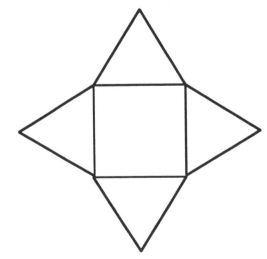

206

b–c. Students cut the lateral faces from the net and tape them together to form the shape of a pyramid. They then measure the height of the pyramid and a side of the base.

d. Students create a right prism with the same base and height as the pyramid in Parts **a–c**.

e. The ratio of the volume of the prism to that of the pyramid should be 3/1. Student results may vary slightly due to measuring and construction errors.

Discussion 2

(page 170)

a. The volume of the prism is three times the volume of a pyramid with the same base and height.

b. The results of the explorations should agree with the formula given in the mathematics note.

c. Sample response: Find the area of the base by squaring s, multiply the area of the base by the height, and multiply that product by 1/3.

d.
1. Students should rank the figures in the following order: right circular cylinder, hemisphere, right circular cone.

2. The volume of the cylinder is $V = B \bullet h = \left(\pi r^2 \right)r = \pi r^3$. The volume of the cone is:

$$V = \frac{1}{3}B \bullet h = \frac{1}{3}\pi r^3$$

3. Conjectures will vary. Based on the formulas for the volume of a cone and a cylinder, students will probably guess that the formula involves the product πr^3. Sample response:

$$V = \frac{2}{3}\pi r^3$$

4. Since the volume of a sphere is twice that of a hemisphere with the same radius, students should suggest multiplying their response to Part **d3** of the discussion by 2.

207

Assignment (page 171)

5.1   **a.** Using the formula for the volume of a cone,

$$V = \frac{1}{3}\pi(10)^2(15) \approx 1571 \text{ cm}^3$$

b. The height of the cylinder must be 1/3 that of the cone, or 5 cm.

c. Students may solve for h as follows:

$$1571 = \frac{1}{3}\pi(8)^2 h$$
$$h \approx 23.4 \text{ cm}$$

5.2   **a.** The area of the regular dodecagon can be found as follows:

$$A = \frac{1}{2}ap = \frac{1}{2}\tan 75°(12 \cdot 2) \approx 45 \text{ m}^2$$

Using the formula for the volume of a pyramid,

$$V \approx \frac{1}{3} \cdot 45 \cdot 5 \approx 75 \text{ m}^3$$

b. $V = \frac{1}{3} \cdot \pi(3.75)^2 5 \approx 74 \text{ m}^3$

c. Sample response: The radius of the dodecagon is approximately 7.4 m, which is close to the radius of the base of the cone. Therefore, the areas of the two bases are close in value. Since the pyramid and the cone have the same height, their volumes are also close in value.

*5.3   **a.** Using the Pythagorean theorem, $h = \sqrt{36 - r^2}$.

b. Students should substitute for h as shown below:

$$V = \frac{1}{3}\pi r^2 h = \frac{1}{3}\pi r^2 \sqrt{36 - r^2}$$

c. The area of the sector is a fraction of the area of the circle with radius 6 m:

$$A = \frac{2\pi r}{12\pi} \cdot \pi(6^2) = 6\pi r$$

d. Sample spreadsheet:

Radius (m)	Volume (m³)	Lateral Surface Area (m²)	Surface Area / Volume
0.1	0.063	1.884	30.004
0.2	0.251	3.768	15.008
⋮	⋮	⋮	⋮
4.1	77.114	77.283	1.002
4.2	79.152	79.168	1.000
4.3	81.023	81.053	1.000
4.4	82.701	82.938	1.003
⋮	⋮	⋮	⋮
5.9	39.765	111.212	2.797

e. Sample response: The smallest ratio of surface area to volume occurs in a cone with a radius somewhere between 4.2 m and 4.3 m. The corresponding range for the heights is also between approximately 4.2 m and 4.3 m.

Teacher Note

The derivation of the formula for the surface area of a sphere requires the use of calculus to find the area of a surface of revolution.

*5.4   **a.** Students should use the diameter of the pit to approximate the radius of the hemisphere. The total volume of the house can be found as follows:

$$V = (\pi \bullet 1.75^2 \bullet 1.5) + \frac{1}{2}\left(\frac{4}{3} \bullet \pi \bullet 1.75^3\right) \approx 25.7 \text{ m}^3$$

b. The total surface area can be found as follows:

$$A = (\pi \bullet 1.75^2) + (2 \bullet \pi \bullet 1.75 \bullet 1.5) + \frac{1}{2}\left(4 \bullet \pi \bullet 1.75^2\right) \approx 45.4 \text{ m}^2$$

c. Sample response: Because part of a pit house is buried—and because the earth provides both insulation and heat storage—it would have less heat loss during cold months, and more moderate indoor temperatures during warm months.

* * * * *

5.5   **a.** The radius of the base of the cone formed by the shaded sector can be determined as shown below:

$$2\pi r = \frac{120°}{360°}(2\pi \bullet 10)$$

$$r \approx 3.3 \text{ cm}$$

The total surface area can be found as follows:

$$A \approx \pi \bullet 3.3^2 + \frac{120°}{360°} \bullet \pi \bullet 10^2 \approx 139 \text{ cm}^2$$

Similarly, the radius of the base of the cone formed by the unshaded sector is:

$$2\pi r = \frac{240°}{360°}(2\pi \bullet 10)$$

$$r \approx 6.7 \text{ cm}$$

The total surface area of this cone is:

$$A \approx \pi \bullet 6.7^2 + \frac{240°}{360°} \bullet \pi \bullet 10^2 \approx 351 \text{ cm}^2$$

b. For the cone formed by the shaded sector, $h \approx \sqrt{10^2 - 3.3^2} \approx 9.4$ cm. Its volume, therefore, is:

$$V \approx \frac{1}{3} \bullet \left(\pi \bullet 3.3^2\right) \bullet 9.4 \approx 107 \text{ cm}^3$$

For the cone formed by the unshaded sector, $h \approx \sqrt{10^2 - 6.7^2} \approx 7.4$ cm. Its volume is:

$$V \approx \frac{1}{3} \bullet \left(\pi \bullet 6.7^2\right) \bullet 7.4 \approx 348 \text{ cm}^3$$

c. For the cone formed by the shaded sector, the ratio is approximately 1.3. For the cone formed by the unshaded sector, the ratio is approximately 1.0.

5.6   **a.** Since the inside radius of the hemisphere is 3 m, its volume is:

$$V = \frac{2}{3}\pi(3^3) \approx 57 \text{ m}^3$$

b. The volume of snow is about 5.9 m^3.

c. The ratio of surface area to volume is approximately 1. Because this ratio is relatively low, one would expect the efficiency to be fairly good—especially when considering the insulating properties of snow. Although some heat will be lost through the floor (which in the Arctic is also frozen), the temperature of the outside air during the cold months is likely to be much lower than that of the tundra.

d. Given a volume of 57 m^3, the length of the half cylinder can be found by solving the following equation for h:

$$57 = \frac{1}{2}(\pi \cdot 3^2 \cdot h)$$

Since $h \approx 4.1 \text{ m}$, the surface area of the half cylinder, not including the floor, is:

$$\pi(3^2) + \pi(3)4.1 \approx 67 \text{ m}^2$$

Therefore, the ratio of surface area to volume is approximately 1.2.

e. Answers will vary. Judging only from the calculated ratios of surface area to volume, the hemisphere should be more efficient to heat than the half cylinder of equal volume.

5.7 **a.** Using the formula for the volume of a sphere,

$$V = \frac{4}{3}\pi(75)^3 \approx 1.8 \cdot 10^6 \text{ cm}^3$$

b. Subtracting the thickness of the walls,

$$V = \frac{4}{3}\pi(75 - 3.8)^3 \approx 1.5 \cdot 10^6 \text{ cm}^3$$

c. The surface area of the Bathysphere is $A = 4\pi(75)^2 \approx 71,00 \text{ cm}^2$, while the surface area of a cube with equal volume would be approximately 88,000 cm^2. Assuming that weight is proportional to surface area, the ratio of the weight of the Bathysphere to the weight of the cube would be approximately 0.8.

* * * * * * * * *

211

Answers to Summary Assessment (page 175)

1.   a. To find the surface area of this structure, students must find the lateral surface area of a cone and the lateral surface area of a cylinder.

   The slant height s of the cone equals $\sqrt{r^2 + h^2}$, where r is the radius of the base and h is the height of the cone. In this case,

   $$s = \sqrt{5.3^2 + 2.5^2} \approx 5.9 \text{ m}$$

   The lateral surface area of the cone, therefore, is:

   $$\pi \cdot r \cdot s = \pi \cdot 5.3 \cdot 5.9 \approx 97 \text{ m}^2$$

   The lateral surface area of the cylinder is:

   $$2\pi \cdot r \cdot h = 2\pi \cdot 5.3 \cdot 2.1 \approx 69 \text{ m}^2$$

   Adding the surface area of the floor ($\pi(5.3^2) \approx 87 \text{ m}^2$), the total surface area is approximately $97 + 69 + 87 = 253 \text{ m}^2$.

   b. The total volume can be found as follows:

   $$V = \frac{1}{3}\pi \cdot 5.3^2 \cdot 2.5 + \pi \cdot 5.3^2 \cdot 2.1 \approx 259 \text{ m}^3$$

2.   The total inside surface area is the surface area of the hemisphere minus the area of the doorway plus the surface area of the entryway. Since the entryway is a half cylinder, its lateral surface area is:

   $$\frac{1}{2}(2\pi \cdot r \cdot h) = \pi \cdot 0.5 \cdot 1 \approx 1.6 \text{ m}^2$$

   The surface area of the hemisphere minus the area of the doorway can be found as follows, where r_i is the radius of the igloo and r_e is the radius of the entryway:

   $$\frac{1}{2}(4\pi r_i^2 - \pi r_e^2) = \frac{1}{2}(4\pi \cdot 2.5^2 - \pi \cdot 0.5^2)$$
   $$\approx 39 \text{ m}^2$$

   The total inside surface area, therefore, is about 41 cm^2.

   The total volume is the sum of the volume of the half cylinder and the volume of the hemisphere:

   $$V = \frac{1}{2}\pi(0.5^2)1 + \frac{1}{2}\left(\frac{4}{3}\pi 2.5^3\right) \approx 33 \text{ m}^3$$

3. **a.** For the Delaware lodge, the total surface area can be found as follows:

$$49 + 4(7 \cdot 3) + 2(7 \cdot 3.9) + 2\left(\frac{1}{2} \cdot 7 \cdot 1.7\right) \approx 200 \text{ m}^2$$

Its volume is:

$$3(49) + \left(\frac{1}{2} \cdot 7 \cdot (1.7) \cdot 7\right) \approx 189 \text{ m}^3$$

The ratio of surface area to volume is approximately 1.

For the Miwok roundhouse, the total surface area is:

$$49 + 2\pi \cdot 3.9 \cdot 3 + \pi(3.9 \cdot 4.3) \approx 175 \text{ m}^2$$

Its volume is:

$$3(49) + \left(\frac{1}{3} \cdot 49 \cdot 1.7\right) \approx 175 \text{ m}^3$$

The ratio of surface area to volume is approximately 1, the same as that for the Delaware lodge.

b. Answers will vary. Sample response: If materials were limited, I would choose the roundhouse. Although it has slightly less volume, it also has less surface area.

c. Answers will vary. Sample response: Judging from ratio of surface area to volume, the two designs appear to be very close in efficiency. The roundhouse might be slightly easier to heat or cool.

1.   Large plank houses were common among the American Indians of the coastal Northwest. The basic shape of this dwelling resembles that of many modern homes. For example, the floor of the plank house in the diagram below is a rectangle that measures 15 m by 18 m. The height of the side walls is 4 m; the height of the roof's peak is 7 m.

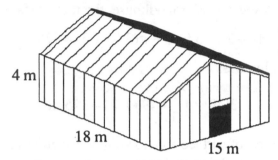

   a. Disregarding the floor, what is the surface area of this house?

   b. What is the volume of this house?

2.   A canvas shop has received an order for some material to cover a tipi. The height of the tipi is 4.5 m. The base of the tipi is an 18-sided regular polygon. Each side measures 1 m. Describe the dimensions of a piece of canvas shaped like a sector of a circle that will cover the tipi.

3.   The Anaconda Company smokestack in Anaconda, Montana, is one of the largest free-standing smokestacks in the world. Its shape approximates a cylinder 178.35 m tall, with an inside diameter of 22.96 m and an outside diameter of 26.21 m.

   a. What volume of building material would be required to build a smokestack of this size?

   b. How does this amount compare to the volume of concrete required to fill a rectangular classroom 7 m wide, 8 m long, and 3 m high ?

4.   Imagine that you are a member of a task force studying the potential colonization of Mars. Since humans cannot survive in the planet's atmosphere, any living area must be enclosed.

   a. Discuss the merits of enclosing living space with a hemisphere compared to a structure of some other shape.

   b. If the distance across the proposed colony is 1 km, how much material will be needed to enclose it with a hemispherical dome?

   c. How much space will the dome contain?

Answers to Module Assessment

1. **a.** The surface area of the lower portion is about 264 m^2; the surface area of the upper portion is about 336 m^2. The total surface area, not including the floor, is approximately 600 m^2.

   b. The volume of the lower portion is about 1080 m^3; the volume of the upper portion is about 405 m^3. The total volume is approximately 1485 m^3.

2. In order to determine the size of the canvas needed for the tipi, students must find the tipi's slant height. Using the Pythagorean theorem, the slant height s equals $\sqrt{r^2 + h^2}$, where r is the radius of the polygonal base (or the circle that circumscribes it) and h is the height of the tipi. The radius can be found using right-triangle trigonometry as follows:

$$r = 0.5/\sin 10° \approx 2.9 \text{ m}$$

   Therefore, the slant height is $s = \sqrt{2.9^2 + 4.5^2} \approx 5.3 \text{ m}$. This value is the radius of the circle from which the sector for the tipi must be cut.

   The arc length that bounds this sector is the circumference of the base of the tipi, or $2\pi(2.9) \approx 18 \text{ m}$. The circumference of the circle is $2\pi(5.3) \approx 33 \text{ m}$. Therefore, the measure of the central angle that defines the sector can be found as follows:

$$x/360° = 18/33$$
$$x \approx 196°$$

   Therefore, the piece of canvas needed for this tipi is a sector of a circle with a radius of 5.3 m whose central angle measures 196°.

3. **a.** The volume of building material is approximately $96,227 - 73,843 = 22,384 \text{ m}^3$.

   b. Since a rectangular classroom with these dimensions has a volume of 168 m^3, the material for the smokestack would completely fill 133 classrooms.

4. **a.** Sample response: Compared to other building shapes, a hemisphere provides a reasonable living space for a given floor area, as well as a low ratio of surface area to volume. One possibility would be a geodesic dome with many sides, thus approaching the advantages of a hemisphere, yet maintaining angles which are easier to build.

   b. The total surface area for this hemisphere (including the floor) is:

$$\frac{1}{2}\left(4\pi(0.5)^2\right) + \pi(0.5)^2 \approx 2.4 \text{ km}^2$$

   c. The volume of a hemisphere with radius 0.5 km is about 0.26 km^3.

Selected References

Blackman, W. *Geometry in Architecture*. Berkeley, CA: Key Curriculum Press, 1984.

Draiver, H. E. *Indians of North America*. Chicago: University of Chicago Press, 1961.

Hall, S. *The Fourth World: The Heritage of the Arctic*. New York: Alfred A. Knopf, Inc., 1987.

Haskin, F. J. *10,000 Answers to Questions*. Detroit, MI: Gale Research Co., 1970.

The 1993 Information Please Almanac. Boston, MA: Houghton Mifflin, 1993.

Laubin, R., and G. Laubin. *The Indian Tipi: Its History, Construction, and Use*. New York: Ballantine Books, 1985.

Maletsky, E. M. "Visualization, Estimation, Computation." *Mathematics Teacher* 75 (December 1982): 759–64.

Maxwell, J., ed. *America's Fascinating Indian Heritage*. Pleasantville, NY: Readers Digest Association, 1978.

Nabokov, P., and R. Easton. *Native American Architecture*. New York: Oxford University Press, 1989.

Flashbacks

Activity 1

1.1   Write the definition of a regular polygon.

1.2   The following diagram shows a regular hexagon inscribed in a circle with a radius of 6 cm. Use this diagram to complete Parts **a–d** below.

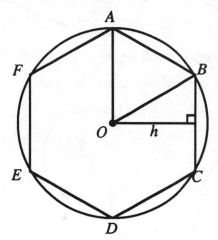

    a.   Find the measure of $\angle AOB$.

    b.   Find h.

    c.   Find the area of the hexagon.

    d.   Find the area of circle O.

Activity 2

2.1   Sketch a net for each of the following figures.

a.   b.   c.

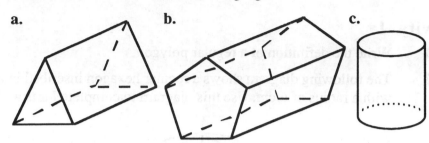

2.2   Describe the bases of each figure in Flashback **2.1**.

2.3   Find the area of each of the following figures.

a.   b.   c.

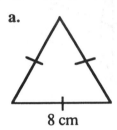   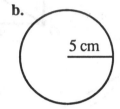   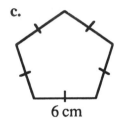

8 cm   5 cm   6 cm

218

Activity 3

3.1 Determine the surface area of the right triangular prism shown below.

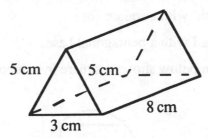

3.2 Find the surface area of the following right pentagonal prism.

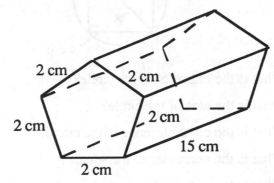

3.3 The diagram below shows half of a right circular cylinder. What is the surface area of this figure?

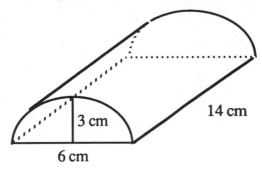

Activity 4

4.1   Sketch a net for each of the following:

     a. a pyramid with a square base

     b. a pyramid with a pentagonal base.

4.2   The diagram below shows a square inscribed in a circle with a radius of 4 cm.

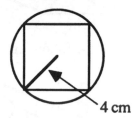

4 cm

     a. What is the diameter of the circle?

     b. What is the area of the circle?

     c. What is the circumference of the circle?

     d. What is the perimeter of the square?

     e. What is the area of the square?

Activity 5

5.1 Solve the following equation for *a*.

$$4^2 = a^2 + b^2$$

5.2 The diagram below shows a right circular cone with a height of 24 cm. The radius of the base is 16 cm.

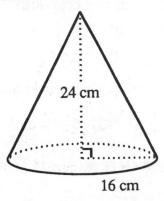

24 cm

16 cm

a. What is the lateral surface area of this cone?

b. What is the total surface area of this cone?

5.3 **a.** Find the surface area, volume, and ratio of surface area to volume for the right square prism shown below.

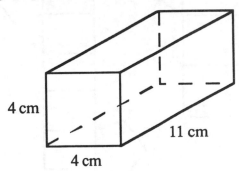

4 cm

11 cm

4 cm

b. Repeat Part **a** for the half of the right circular cylinder in the following diagram.

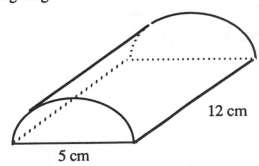

12 cm

5 cm

Answers to Flashbacks

Activity 1

1.1 Sample response: A regular polygon is a polygon in which all angles are congruent and all sides are congruent.

1.2 **a.** $m\angle AOB = 60°$ is 60°.

    b. $h = 3\sqrt{3} \approx 5.2$ cm

    c. The area of the hexagon is six times the area of $\triangle AOB$:

$$\frac{1}{2}(6 \cdot 3\sqrt{3}) \cdot 6 \approx 94 \text{ cm}^2$$

    d. The area of the circle is $\pi(6^2) \approx 113 \text{ cm}^2$.

Activity 2

2.1 Sample sketches:

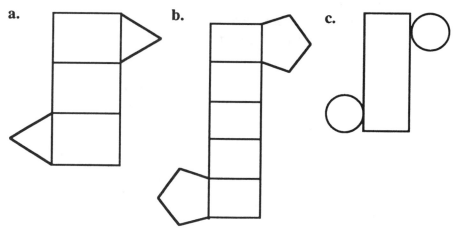

2.2 **a.** The bases are triangles.

    b. The bases are pentagons.

    c. The bases are circles.

2.3   **a.** Using the formula for the area of a triangle,

$$\frac{1}{2} \cdot 8 \cdot 4\sqrt{3} \approx 27.7 \text{ cm}^2$$

b. $\pi(5^2) \approx 78.5 \text{ cm}^2$

c. Using the formula for the area of a regular polygon,

$$\frac{1}{2}\left(\frac{3}{\tan 36°}\right)(6 \cdot 5) \approx 62 \text{ cm}^2$$

Activity 3

3.1   The surface area can be found as follows:

$$\frac{4.8 \cdot 3}{2} \cdot 2 + (5 + 5 + 3)8 \approx 118 \text{ cm}^2$$

3.2   The surface area can be found as follows:

$$\left(\frac{(1/\tan 36°) \cdot 2}{2} \cdot 5\right) \cdot 2 + 15 \cdot 2 \cdot 5 \approx 164 \text{ cm}^2$$

3.3   The surface area can be found as follows:

$$\pi \cdot 3^2 + \frac{1}{2}(2\pi \cdot 3 \cdot 14) \approx 160 \text{ cm}^2.$$

Activity 4

4.1   Sample sketches:

a. 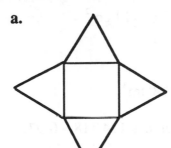   b.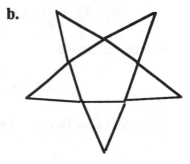

4.2　**a.** The diameter of the circle is 8 cm.

　　　b. The area of the circle is approximately $\pi(4^2) \approx 50$ cm^2.

　　　c. The circumference of the circle is approximately $2\pi(4) \approx 25$ cm.

　　　d. The perimeter of the square is:

$$\frac{8}{\sqrt{2}} \cdot 4 \approx 23 \text{ cm}$$

　　　e. The area of the square is:

$$\frac{8}{\sqrt{2}} \cdot \frac{8}{\sqrt{2}} \approx 32 \text{ cm}^2$$

Activity 5

5.1　$a = \sqrt{4^2 - b^2}$ or $a = -\sqrt{4^2 - b^2}$

5.2　**a.** The slant height of the cone is $\sqrt{24^2 + 16^2} \approx 29$ cm. The lateral surface area of the cone is $\pi \cdot 16 \cdot 29 \approx 1460$ cm^2.

　　　b. The total surface area of the cone is approximately $\pi \cdot 16 \cdot 29 + \pi \cdot 16^2 \approx 2260$ cm^2.

5.3　**a.** The surface area is $2 \cdot 4 \cdot 4 + 4 \cdot 11 \cdot 4 = 208$ cm^2 and the volume is $4 \cdot 11 \cdot 4 = 176$ cm^3. The ratio of surface area to volume is $208/176 \approx 1.2$.

　　　b. The surface area is

$$\pi(2.5)^2 + \frac{1}{2}(2\pi \cdot 2.5 \cdot 12) \approx 114 \text{ cm}^2$$

and the volume is

$$\frac{1}{2}\pi(2.5)^2 \cdot 12 \approx 118 \text{ cm}^3$$

The ratio of surface area to volume is $114/118 \approx 0.97$.

Making Concessions

If there's going to be a prom this spring, the class needs to raise some cash. What to sell? How much to buy? How much to charge? Unless the class makes good choices, the big spring dance could be doomed.

Bonnie Eichenberger • Paul Swenson

Making Concessions

Overview
Students examine linear programming in two dimensions and in three dimensions. To find corner points of figures that enclose feasible solutions, they solve systems of linear equations using substitution and matrices.

Objectives
In this module, students will:

- determine constraints for linear programming problems
- write objective functions
- interpret the meaning of points in a feasible region
- find the corner points of a feasible region
- develop the corner principle for optimization
- find solutions to systems of inequalities in two variables
- solve systems of equations in two and three variables graphically, algebraically (by substitution), and by using matrices
- use linear programming to make decisions involving the buying and selling of goods.

Prerequisites
For this module, students should know:

- how to graph inequalities on a number line
- how to graph inequalities on a coordinate plane
- how to write the equation of a line
- how to solve a system of linear equations involving two variables using substitution
- how to multiply matrices.

Time Line

Activity	1	2	3	4	Summary Assessment	Total
Days	2	3	2	3	1	11

Materials Required

Materials	Activity				
	1	2	3	4	Summary Assessment
graph paper	X	X	X		
cardboard box				X	
scissors				X	
tape				X	

Technology

Software	Activity				
	1	2	3	4	Summary Assessment
graphing utility	X	X	X		
3-D graphing utility				X	
matrix manipulator			X	X	

Teacher Note

In Activity **4**, students model feasible regions in three dimensions. This may be treated as an optional activity.

228

Making Concessions

Introduction (page 181)

In this module, students use feasibility studies and linear programming to help plan concession sales.

(page 181)

Activity 1

This activity focuses on a typical decision-making process in a business setting. Students represent ranges of values on number-line graphs. They then use these ranges to establish feasible regions for linear programming problems.

Materials List

- graph paper (several sheets per student; optional)

Technology

- graphing utility (optional)

Teacher Note

The sample data given in the following exploration will be used to generate sample responses throughout the module.

Exploration (page 181)

Students consider some basic questions concerning the planning and start-up of a concession stand. This works well as a group activity.

a–e.   Students make decisions based on their own experiences and wishes. The only restriction is the $100 spending limit. The profits shown in the following sample table assume that all items are sold:

Item	How Sold	Selling Price	Cost per Item	Quantity Purchased	Amount Spent	Potential Profit
pizza	by piece	$2.00	$5.00	10 pizzas	$50.00	$110.00
pop	by can	$1.00	$2.00	15 six-packs	$30.00	$60.00
nachos	by weight	$1.50	$10.00	2 kits	$20.00	$28.00
				Total	$100.00	$198.00

f.   Students write summaries of their recommendations. **Note:** Students use their data on quantity and profit in the assignment.

229

Discussion

(page 182)

a. Since students have no indication of the potential market or acceptable selling prices, they may have some difficulty deciding how much of each item to buy and how much to charge.

b. Sample response: It would have helped to know the number of people who would buy concessions, the number interested in each item, the cost to the class for each item, the number of home games left, and the availability of storage for unused products.

c. Questions should reflect student concerns in Parts **a** and **b**.

d. Sample response: We assumed that the items could be obtained for a certain price, that we would not have to rent selling space, and that all the food would be sold.

e. **1–2.** Answers will vary. Some students may recommend that none of a particular item be bought. The greatest recommended number must keep the total cost below $100.

3. Sample response: The profit ranges from $40 to $600.

f. Since it is possible to spend $100 and not sell anything, the least possible profit is –$100.

Assignment

(page 182)

1.1 **a.** Sample response: The profit could range from –$100 to $600.

b. Sample graph:

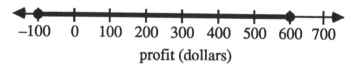

profit (dollars)

c. Answers will vary. The sample response given in Part **a** can be written as –$100 ≤ profit ≤ $600.

d. Sample response: I used the symbols ≤ and ≥ because the endpoints of the interval were part of the range of values.

1.2 **a.** **1.** Point *A* represents the purchase of 20 pizzas and 30 six-packs.

2. Point *B* represents the purchase of 20 pizzas and 0 six-packs.

b. Sample response: The *x*-coordinate of point *C* is always between 5 and 20. The *y*-coordinate can take on any real-number value.

230

c. Sample response: The shaded region below the *x*-axis has no meaning because it is impossible to buy a negative number of six-packs. Since you can't buy fractions of pizzas or six-packs, any points with non-integer coordinates also have no meaning.

Because the class has only $100 to spend, the shaded region above the number of six-packs that can be purchased for $100 is not relevant in this setting.

d. Sample graph:

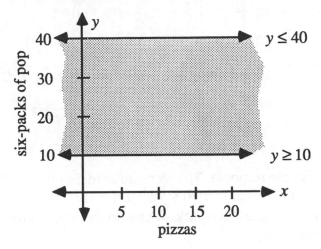

e. Sample graph:

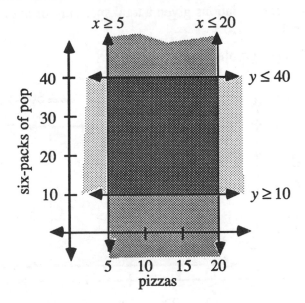

231

1.3   Answers will vary, depending on the class data. The following sample responses are based on ranges of 5–20 pizzas and 10–50 six-packs.

a. Sample graph:

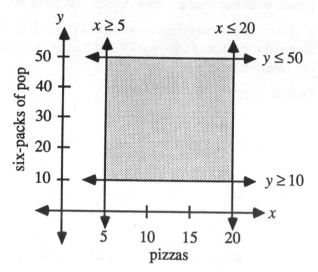

b. Sample response: The rectangular region formed by the intersection of $5 \leq x \leq 20$ and $10 \leq y \leq 50$ shows all the possible combinations of pizzas and six-packs where no more than $100 is spent on either pizza or pop.

Note: A point such as (20,50) would not meet class recommendations given a total spending limit of $100. (See Problem **1.6**.)

1.4   **a.** Sample graph:

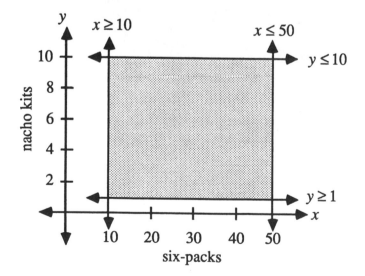

232

b. Sample graph:

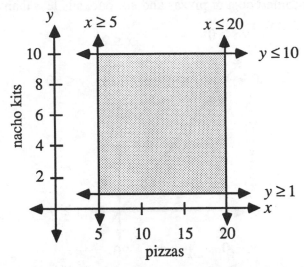

1.5   **a**. For the sample graph given in Problem **1.2e**, the intersection is the set of all ordered pairs such that $5 \leq x \leq 20$ and $10 \leq y \leq 40$.

  b. Since the boundary lines represent values that satisfy the constraints, the symbols $\leq$ and $\geq$ should be used.

  c. Sample response: No. Pizzas, six-packs, and nacho kits can only be bought in whole numbers, so only points whose coordinates are integers [lattice points] should be considered.

*1.6   **a**. Sample response: Medium pizzas cost $5.00 each and pop costs $2.00 per six-pack. **Note:** The sample responses given below are based on these costs.

  b. **1**. $0 \leq x \leq 20$

    2. $0 \leq y \leq 50$

    3. See sample graph given in Part **d** below.

  c. **1**. Sample response: $5x + 2y \leq 100$.

    2. See sample graph given in Part **d** below.

233

d. The shaded area in the following sample graph indicates where the combined cost of pizzas and six-packs is less than or equal to $100.

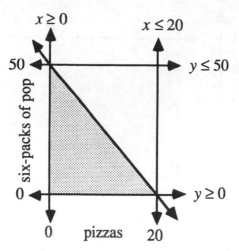

e. 1. The coordinates of the corner points in the sample graph above are (0,50), (20,0), and (0,0).

2. Student responses may include descriptions of graphing and tracing, solving a system of linear equations by substitution, or the use of a symbolic manipulator.

* * * * *

1.7   a. In the following sample responses, x represents the number of boys and y represents the number of girls.

1. $x \geq 30$

2. $y \geq 30$

3. $x + y \leq 120$

4. $5y \geq 7x$

b–c. As shown in the sample graph below, all of the corner points are in the feasible region.

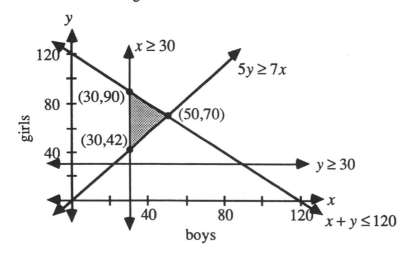

234

1.8   **a.** $x > 0$, $y \geq 30$, $x + y \leq 70$, and $y \geq x$.

   b. The corner points are (30,30), (35,35), (0,70), and (0,30). Corner points (30,30) and (35,35) lie within the feasible region.

   c. Sample response: The constraints indicate that no more than 70 students will be surveyed. Of those surveyed, the number of girls must be greater than or equal to the number of boys. There must be at least 30 girls interviewed.

* * * * * * * * *

(page 186)

Activity 2

Students continue to graph feasible regions and identify the corner points. They then explore the use of the corner principle for solving linear programming problems.

Materials List

   • graph paper (several sheets per student; optional)

Technology

   • graphing utility

Exploration 1   (page 187)

   a. Students explore how the graph of an objective function is affected as the value of the objective (in this case, profit) changes.

   b.   **1.** Students should observe that all the lines are parallel.

   2. Sample response: As the value of P increases, so does the y-intercept.

Discussion 1   (page 187)

   a. Sample response: The lines are parallel (they all have the same slope).

   b. Sample response: The slope of the line represented by $P = 3x + 2y$ is the ratio of its y-coefficient to its x-coefficient. In all the lines we graphed, the x-coefficient and y-coefficient remained the same.

   c. Sample response: For a given profit function, the value of P remains constant. As the value of x increases, the value of y decreases.

   d. Sample response: The graph representing the greatest profit is located above the others. This happens because the value of P affects the y-intercept. The greater the value of P in the objective function, the greater the y-intercept.

235

e.   Sample response: The graph that represents the least profit is the one with the lowest y-intercept in the feasible region. This line is located below the others.

Exploration 2   (page 187)

a.   Sample graph:

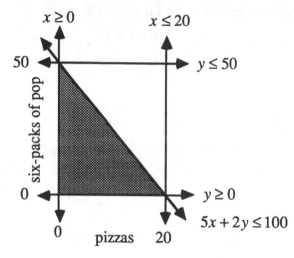

b.   **1.** Sample response: The point $(10,25)$ lies in the feasible region. Substituting these values in the equation $P = 3x + 2y$ yields $P = 80$.

       2. Substituting 80 for P results in the equation $80 = 3x + 2y$.

c.   **1.** The line that indicates the maximum profit intersects the feasible region at the corner point $(0,50)$.

       2. Since the equation of this line is $100 = 3x + 2y$, the maximum profit is $100.

d.   Students compare values for maximum profit with others in the class.

Discussion 2   (page 188)

a.   **1.** Two lines must intersect to determine a vertex.

       2. Two equations are needed to find the coordinates of the vertex.

b.   Many graphing utilities will only graph functions. Constraints in the form $x = c$, where c is a constant, are not functions.

c.   The line that indicates the maximum profit passes through the corner point $(0,50)$. All other lines that pass through the feasible region are below that line.

d. Sample response: To find the coordinates of the vertex in the lower right-hand corner of the feasible region, for example, you can use the lines defined by the equations $5x + 2y = 100$ and $x = 20$ (the two intersecting boundary lines). Substituting 20 for the value of x in the equation $5x + 2y = 100$ results in $5(20) + 2y = 100$. Solving this equation for y yields $y = 0$. Since the point with coordinates $(20,0)$ satisfies both equations, it is a point of intersection and thus a corner point of the feasible region.

e. Sample response: You could find the coordinates for all the corner points of the feasible region and substitute the values of the coordinates into the objective function until you found the greatest value for P.

f. Sample response: The graph of the objective function that maximizes the objective would coincide with the edge of the feasible region. The maximum value would occur at any point along that border, so there might be more than one way to maximize the objective function.

g. The maximum profit can be found by substituting the coordinates into the objective function.

h. Sample response: Since $5/8$ of a six-pack is equivalent to $3\frac{3}{4}$ cans, this is not a possible amount to buy.

i. Sample response: This means that the maximum value occurs at any point on the segment joining $(0,4)$ and $(3,3)$.

Assignment

(page 190)

2.1 Since lines b and c appear to be parallel, they could represent the same profit function for different values of P.

2.2   **a.** Sample graph for Parts **1–4**:

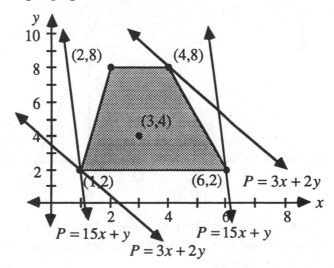

1. $28 = 3(4) + 2(8)$

2. $92 = 15(6) + 2$

3. $7 = 3(1) + 2(2)$

4. $P = 15(1) + 2$

    b. Sample response: The slope of the objective function determines which corner point of the feasible region represents a maximum or minimum value of the function.

*2.3   **a.** The constraints on the problem can be represented by the inequalities $0 \le x \le 16$, $0 \le y \le 22$, and $4.96x + 1.84y \le 100$ where x represents the number of pizzas and y represents the number of six-packs of pop.

    b. See sample graph given in Part **e** below.

    c. The profit is $11.04 on each pizza and $4.16 on each six-pack.

    d. Sample response: $P = 11.04x + 4.16y$, where P is profit, x is the number of pizzas, and y is the number of six-packs.

    e. The maximum value of $P = 11.04x + 4.16y$ occurs at the corner point (12,22). If all items are sold, the maximum profit is $12(11.04) + 22(4.16)$ or $224.00. Sample graph:

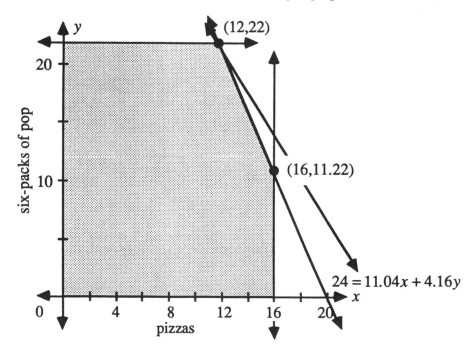

    f. Sample response: The class should buy 12 pizzas and 22 six-packs of pop. Since these are whole number quantities, this seems to be a reasonable answer.

2.4   **a.** Substituting 5.5 for x in each equation yields the following:

$$y_1 = 0.8(5.5) + 4$$
$$= 4.4 + 4$$
$$= 8.4$$

$$y_2 = -(5.5) + 13.9$$
$$= 8.4$$

Therefore, $(5.5, 8.4)$ is a solution to both equations.

b. The coordinates of the corner points are $A(0,0)$, $B(0,4)$, $D(8.4, 5.5)$, and $E(8.95, 0)$. Students should verify these coordinates by substituting them in the equations defining the corresponding boundaries of the feasible region.

3.4   **a.** Sample graph:

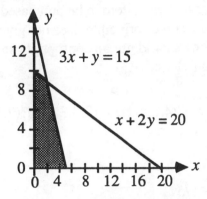

b. The coordinates of the corner points are $(0,0)$, $(5,0)$, $(2,9)$, and $(0,10)$.

c. **1.** As shown in the table below, the minimum of -5 occurs at $(5,0)$.

(x, y)	$P = 2y - x$	$P = 3y + 2x$
$(0,0)$	0	0
$(5,0)$	-5	10
$(2,9)$	16	31
$(0,10)$	20	30

2. As shown in the table above, the minimum of 0 occurs at $(0,0)$.

2.6   **a.** The maximum value of the objective function occurs at the corner point $\left(9\frac{1}{3}, 22\right)$, where x represents number of pizzas and y represents number of six-packs. Since the value for x is not a whole number, it does represent a reasonable amount of pizza to buy.

b. To find the maximum profit which corresponds to a point with integer coordinates, students may suggest rounding solutions to the nearest integer or substituting the coordinates of points near the corner point into the objective function.

In this case, the point (9,22) results in a profit of $244. Although the points (10,22) and (10,21) produce greater profits, they are not in the feasible region. The point (10,20) is in the feasible bur results in a profit of only $240.

Note: Neither of these methods guarantee that the optimum value will be found.

c. Sample response: A businessperson might buy less if the profit is not greatly affected. They may buy slightly more if they believe they could sell the extra or easily absorb the loss.

2.7 Answers will vary. Students should record the quantities of cheese and chips needed to make an appropriate number of nacho servings, the quantity and cost of each item to be purchased, and the selling price of each item. If the corner principle does not give a solution with integer coordinates, they should use an appropriate strategy to determine the quantities to purchase.

* * * * *

2.8 $A(0,0)$, $B(0,5)$, $C(4.2,7.1)$, $D(9.3,3.7)$, $E(7.45,0)$

2.9 a. 1. $D(10,8)$

2. $A(0,0)$

b. 1. $m = -8/5$

2. At both D and E, the value of the objective function is 120.

3. The equation of this line in slope-intercept form is:

$$y = -\frac{8}{5}x + \frac{P}{5}$$

The slope of the objective function is $-8/5$.

4. Since the slope of the objective function is the same as the slope of the line that passes through D and E, the value of the function is the same at both D and E (and at any other point on $\overline{DE}$).

5. All three lines would be parallel to $\overline{DE}$.

c. 1. Sample response: $P = 2x + 5y$.

2. Sample response: $P = x + 5y$.

3. Sample response: $P = 10x + 2y$.

* * * * * * * * *

Students plan a fund-raiser that involves selling two different items. To help determine the feasibility of their plan, they conduct a survey. They then prepare a report designed to persuade their classmates to invest in the venture. This works well as a small-group activity.

You may wish to allow students to implement a plan selected by the class. Students then can evaluate the accuracy of their projections.

(page 194)

Activity 3

Students use matrices to solve systems of two equations in two unknowns. Matrix equations are then used to find corner points of feasible regions.

Materials
- graph paper (several sheets per student)

Technology
- graphing utility
- matrix manipulator

Exploration (page 194)

Students examine the relationship between a system of two equations and two unknowns and the corresponding matrix equation. The concept of inverse matrices is introduced. Students than use technology to solve matrix equations.

a. Students should obtain the following equation:
$$\begin{bmatrix} -8x & 10y \\ 10x & 10y \end{bmatrix} = \begin{bmatrix} 40 \\ 139 \end{bmatrix}$$

b. Sample response: The entries in the matrices are the terms of the equations. The first equation's terms are in the top rows of the matrices; the second equation's terms are in the bottom rows of the matrices.

c. One way for students to verify the value of M^{-1} is to enter matrix M in their technology, then use the multiplicative inverse command. A second approach involves entering both M and M^{-1}, then finding their product—which should be the identity matrix.

241

d. Matrices will vary. Sample response:

$$\begin{bmatrix} 6 & 4 \\ -2 & 5 \end{bmatrix} \bullet \begin{bmatrix} 1 & 0 \\ 0 & 1 \end{bmatrix} = \begin{bmatrix} 1 & 0 \\ 0 & 1 \end{bmatrix} \bullet \begin{bmatrix} 6 & 4 \\ -2 & 5 \end{bmatrix} = \begin{bmatrix} 6 & 4 \\ -2 & 5 \end{bmatrix}$$

$$\begin{bmatrix} 8 & 3 \\ 10 & -5 \end{bmatrix} \bullet \begin{bmatrix} 1 & 0 \\ 0 & 1 \end{bmatrix} = \begin{bmatrix} 1 & 0 \\ 0 & 1 \end{bmatrix} \bullet \begin{bmatrix} 8 & 3 \\ 10 & -5 \end{bmatrix} = \begin{bmatrix} 8 & 3 \\ 10 & -5 \end{bmatrix}$$

e. **1.** The matrix equation is shown below:

$$\begin{bmatrix} 5 & 2 \\ 2 & 1 \end{bmatrix} \bullet \begin{bmatrix} x \\ y \end{bmatrix} = \begin{bmatrix} 22 \\ 9 \end{bmatrix}$$

2. The inverse of the coefficient matrix is:

$$\begin{bmatrix} 1 & -2 \\ -2 & 5 \end{bmatrix}$$

3. The resulting equation is:

$$\begin{bmatrix} 1 & -2 \\ -2 & 5 \end{bmatrix} \bullet \begin{bmatrix} 5 & 2 \\ 2 & 1 \end{bmatrix} \bullet \begin{bmatrix} x \\ y \end{bmatrix} = \begin{bmatrix} 1 & -2 \\ -2 & 5 \end{bmatrix} \bullet \begin{bmatrix} 22 \\ 9 \end{bmatrix}$$

$$\begin{bmatrix} x \\ y \end{bmatrix} = \begin{bmatrix} 4 \\ 1 \end{bmatrix}$$

4. The matrix equation verifies the solution:

$$\begin{bmatrix} 5 & 2 \\ 2 & 1 \end{bmatrix} \bullet \begin{bmatrix} 4 \\ 1 \end{bmatrix} = \begin{bmatrix} 22 \\ 9 \end{bmatrix}$$

5. The solution is (4,1).

6. Students should substitute as follows:

$$5(4) + 2y_1 = 22 \qquad 2(4) + y_2 = 9$$
$$20 + 2y_1 = 22 \qquad 8 + y_2 = 9$$
$$y_1 = 1 \qquad y_2 = 1$$

Therefore, (4,1) is a solution to both equations.

7. Since the graphs of the two lines intersect at (4,1), the graph verifies the solution.

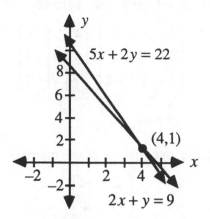

f. **1.** The system is inconsistent because the graphs are parallel and do not have a common point.

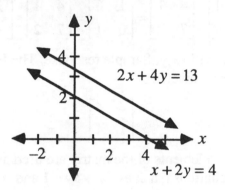

2. The process fails because the coefficient matrix does not have an inverse.

Discussion

(page 197)

a. Sample response: You can enter the coefficient matrix **M** and use the multiplicative inverse button to find $\mathbf{M}^{-1}$. Or you can enter **M** and $\mathbf{M}^{-1}$, then find their product to see if you get the identity matrix.

b. The coefficient matrix does not have an inverse.

c. The coefficient matrix is a 2×2 matrix with a y coefficient equal to 0:

$$\begin{bmatrix} 3 & 0 \\ 5 & 2 \end{bmatrix}$$

d. Sample response: Matrix multiplication is not commutative. In matrix multiplication, the number of columns in the first matrix must equal the number of rows in the second matrix. The coefficient matrix must be multiplied by the inverse matrix on the left in order for the dimensions to match.

e. Using a process similar to that described for systems of two equations and two unknowns, the system can be represented as a matrix equation in the form $\mathbf{M \cdot X = C}$ as shown below:

$$\begin{bmatrix} 1 & 1 & 1 \\ 2 & -1 & 1 \\ 1 & 3 & -2 \end{bmatrix} \cdot \begin{bmatrix} x \\ y \\ z \end{bmatrix} = \begin{bmatrix} 6 \\ 15 \\ -7 \end{bmatrix}$$

Assignment (page 198)

3.1   **a.** The multiplicative inverse of the matrix is shown below:

$$\begin{bmatrix} 2 & -1 \\ -7 & 4 \end{bmatrix}$$

   b. Sample response:

$$\begin{bmatrix} 2 & -1 \\ -7 & 4 \end{bmatrix} \cdot \begin{bmatrix} 4 & 1 \\ 7 & 2 \end{bmatrix} = \begin{bmatrix} 1 & 0 \\ 0 & 1 \end{bmatrix} = \begin{bmatrix} 4 & 1 \\ 7 & 2 \end{bmatrix} \cdot \begin{bmatrix} 2 & -1 \\ -7 & 4 \end{bmatrix}$$

   c. Answers will vary. Sample response: The following matrix does not have an inverse.

$$\begin{bmatrix} 2 & 8 \\ 1 & 4 \end{bmatrix}$$

   When the elements of the matrix are used as coefficients, the graphs of the equations (such as $2x + 8y = 1$ and $x + 4y = 3$) are parallel. When I try to find the multiplicative inverse using technology, I get an error message.

3.2   Students can verify their solutions by substituting the values obtained into the original equations.

   a. $\begin{bmatrix} x \\ y \end{bmatrix} = \begin{bmatrix} 3 \\ 5 \end{bmatrix}$

   b. $\begin{bmatrix} x \\ y \end{bmatrix} = \begin{bmatrix} -1 \\ 7 \end{bmatrix}$

   c. $\begin{bmatrix} x \\ y \end{bmatrix} = \begin{bmatrix} 4 \\ 2 \end{bmatrix}$

3.3

$$\begin{bmatrix} 80 & 33 \\ -20 & 73 \end{bmatrix} \bullet \begin{bmatrix} x \\ y \end{bmatrix} = \begin{bmatrix} 466 \\ 46 \end{bmatrix}$$

$$\begin{bmatrix} 80 & 33 \\ -20 & 73 \end{bmatrix}^{-1} \bullet \left(\begin{bmatrix} 80 & 33 \\ -20 & 73 \end{bmatrix} \bullet \begin{bmatrix} x \\ y \end{bmatrix} \right) = \begin{bmatrix} 80 & 33 \\ -20 & 73 \end{bmatrix}^{-1} \bullet \begin{bmatrix} 466 \\ 46 \end{bmatrix}$$

$$\begin{bmatrix} x \\ y \end{bmatrix} = \begin{bmatrix} 5 \\ 2 \end{bmatrix}$$

3.4   **a.** Sample graph:

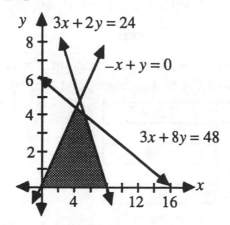

b. $(0,0)$, $(8,0)$, $\left(5\frac{1}{3}, 4\right)$, $\left(4\frac{4}{11}, 4\frac{4}{11}\right)$

c. As shown in the table below, the maximum of 24 occurs at two corner points. Therefore, the maximum occurs at any point on the segment connecting these two points.

(x,y)	$P = 2y + 3x$
$(0,0)$	0
$(8,0)$	24
$\left(5\frac{1}{3}, 4\right)$	24
$\left(4\frac{4}{11}, 4\frac{4}{11}\right)$	$21\frac{9}{11}$

*3.5   **a.** In the following inequalities, x represents number of pizzas and y represents number of six-packs:

$$5x + 2y \leq 100$$
$$2y \geq 10$$
$$5x \leq 80$$
$$5x \leq 8y$$
$$x \geq 0$$

b. Sample graph:

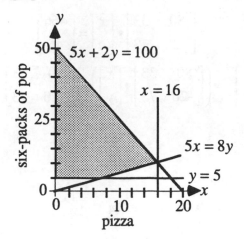

c. As shown below, the profit function $P = 11x + 2y$ has its maximum value at the corner point (16,10).

(x,y)	$P = 11x + 2y$
(0,5)	10
(8,5)	98
(16,10)	196
(0,50)	100

The maximum potential profit of $196 occurs if the class buys (and sells) 16 pizzas and 10 six-packs.

* * * * *

3.6   **a.** In the following inequalities, x represents millions of liters from the reservoir and y represents millions of liters from the aquifer.

$$x + y \geq 20$$
$$x \leq 12$$
$$y \geq 14$$
$$y \leq 20$$
$$x \geq 0$$

b. In the following sample graph, units on the axes represent millions of liters. The feasible region is shaded.

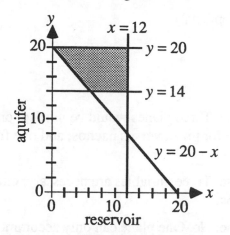

c. As shown below, the minimum value of the objective function $C = 80x + 100y$ occurs at the corner point (6,14). The maximum occurs at the point (12,20).

(x,y)	$C = 80x + 100y$
(0,20)	2000
(6,14)	1880
(12,14)	2360
(12,20)	2960

1. $1880

2. $2960

* * * * * * * * * *

(page 200)

Activity 4

Students extend linear programming concepts into three dimensions by considering the sale of three items instead of two. **Note:** This may be treated as an optional activity.

Materials List

- cardboard boxes (one per group)
- scissors (one pair per group)
- tape

247

Technology

- 3-D graphing utility (optional)
- matrix manipulator

Discussion 1 (page 200)

a. Sample response: Three planes would be needed: one to graph pizza versus pop, one for pizza versus nachos, and one for pop versus nachos.

b. Sample response: Three variables are necessary: one each for pizza, pop, and nachos.

c. Sample response: No. One plane can only accommodate two different variables.

d. Sample response: The constraints for three items could be displayed on a three-dimensional coordinate system where planes would represent the boundaries.

Teacher Note

You may wish to discuss the various ways in which three planes can intersect one another. These are illustrated below.

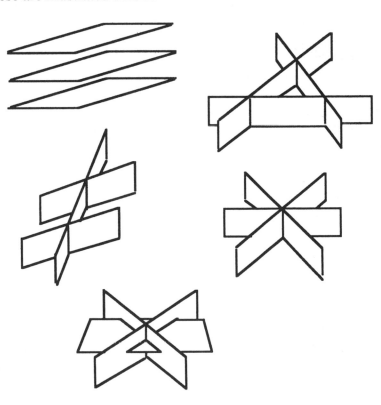

248

Exploration

(page 200)

Students build a model of the first octant of a three-dimensional coordinate system. This activity works well in small groups.

a–b.   Students cut cardboard boxes and label the axes of their coordinate systems. **Note:** The leftover cardboard should be saved for use in Part **d**.

c–d.   On each plane surface of the first octant, students shade one of three regions defined by inequalities. They then cut a model of each region from the leftover pieces of cardboard.

e.   Students move the model of region A through the various values of the constraint placed on z.

f.   Students should tape the model regions to form a rectangular prism in the first octant. This prism defines the set of feasible solutions for the constraints $0 \leq x \leq 6$, $0 \leq y \leq 4$, and $0 \leq z \leq 5$.

g.   The coordinates of the eight corner points are: (0,0,0), (0,0,5), (6,0,0), (6,0,5), (0,4,0), (0,4,5), (6,4,0), and (6,4,5).

Discussion 2

(page 201)

a.   The set of points is described by the constraints $0 \leq y \leq 4$ and $0 \leq x \leq 6$, with $z = 1$, $z = 2$, ..., $z = 5$.

b.   **1.** Three planes may intersect in a single point. Two planes may intersect in a line.

   2. Each corner point is formed from the intersection of three planes. There are four ways in which three planes can be selected from four planes: ABC, ABD, ACD, and BCD.

   3. The maximum number of corner points is 10. Given five planes A, B, C, D, and E, the 10 possible sets of three planes are ABC, ABD, ABE, ACD, ACE, ADE, BCD, BCE, BDE, and CDE.

c.   **1.** The shape is a rectangular prism. A rectangular prism has eight vertices.

   2. Sample response: No. Not all sets of constraints that involve six planes would have three pairs of parallel planes. The parallel planes reduce the number of possible corner points.

d.   **1.** Sample response: By the corner principle, the maximum will occur at one of the eight corner points. The specific point where the maximum occurs would depend on the objective function.

   2. Sample response: The coordinates of each corner point could be substituted into the objective function to determine which represents the maximum value.

e.   Sample response: No, this would require four dimensions.

4.1   **a.** This graph shows the constraints on pizza and pop. The shaded region is defined by $0 \le x \le 10$, $0 \le y \le 12$, and $z = 0$.

b. This graph shows the constraints on pop and nachos. The shaded region is defined by $0 \le y \le 12$, $0 \le z \le 14$, and $x = 0$.

c. This graph shows the constraints on pizza and nachos. The shaded region is defined by $0 \le x \le 10$, $0 \le z \le 14$, and $y = 0$.

4.2   Sample response: The class should purchase from 0 to 10 pizzas, from 0 to 12 six-packs of pop, and from 0 to 14 nacho kits.

4.3   **a.** $y = 12$, $y = 0$, $z = 14$, $z = 0$

b. $x = 10$, $x = 0$, $z = 14$, $z = 0$

c. Sample response: The points of intersection consist of all the possible combinations of ordered triples formed by the x-values, y-values, and z-values of the equations.

4.4   Sample sketch:

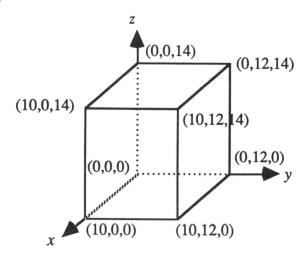

4.5   As shown in the table below, the maximum value of $P = x + y + z$ occurs at the point (10,12,14).

(x,y,z)	$P = x + y + z$
(0,0,0)	0
(10,0,0)	10
(0,12,0)	12
(0,0,14)	14
(10,12,0)	22
(10,0,14)	24
(0,12,14	26
(10,12,14)	36

4.6 **a.** (–11,–3,9)

     b. This system is inconsistent.

     c. $\left(\dfrac{23}{5},-\dfrac{8}{5},-\dfrac{1}{5}\right)$ or $(4.6,-1.6,-0.2)$

4.7 **a.** The profit is $11.00 on each pizza, $4.00 on each six-pack of pop, and $14.00 on each nacho kit.

     b. $P = 11x + 4y + 14z$

*4.8 **a.** The constraints are $0 \le x \le 10$, $0 \le y \le 25$, and $0 \le z \le 5$.

     b. Six planes enclose the feasible solutions.

     c. Sample response: Eight points must be examined to find the maximum profit. There are eight corner points because the figure formed by the planes is a rectangular prism. **Note:** Students who do not visualize the prism may respond that 20 points must be examined (the maximum number of ways in which six planes can be chosen three at a time).

4.9 The maximum value of $P = 11x + 4y + 14z$ occurs at the corner point $(10,25,5)$. The profit at this point is $11(10) + 4(25) + 14(5) = \$280$.

* * * * *

4.10 Answers will vary. Students should record the cost and number of each item to be purchased, the number of servings that can be produced from each one, the selling prices, and the profit.

4.11 The solution may be found as follows:

$$\begin{bmatrix} 1 & 1 & 1 \\ 2 & 1 & 2 \\ 5 & 2 & 3 \end{bmatrix} \cdot \begin{bmatrix} x \\ y \\ z \end{bmatrix} = \begin{bmatrix} 15 \\ 26 \\ 43 \end{bmatrix}$$

$$\begin{bmatrix} 1 & 1 & 1 \\ 2 & 1 & 2 \\ 5 & 2 & 3 \end{bmatrix}^{-1} \cdot \begin{bmatrix} 1 & 1 & 1 \\ 2 & 1 & 2 \\ 5 & 2 & 3 \end{bmatrix} \cdot \begin{bmatrix} x \\ y \\ z \end{bmatrix} = \begin{bmatrix} 1 & 1 & 1 \\ 2 & 1 & 2 \\ 5 & 2 & 3 \end{bmatrix}^{-1} \cdot \begin{bmatrix} 15 \\ 26 \\ 43 \end{bmatrix}$$

$$\begin{bmatrix} x \\ y \\ z \end{bmatrix} = \begin{bmatrix} 1 \\ 4 \\ 10 \end{bmatrix}$$

* * * * * * * * * *

Answers to Summary Assessment (page 204)

1. Sample response: Let x represent the number of double hamburgers and y represent the number of single hamburgers. The following inequalities are the constraints that define the feasible region:
   $0.2x + 0.1y \leq 20$, $x \geq 0$, $y \geq 0$, $x \leq 90$, $y \leq 100$, and $8x + 6y \leq 960$.

   The profit function is the equation $p = 0.90x + 0.70y$.

   The graph below shows the feasible region.

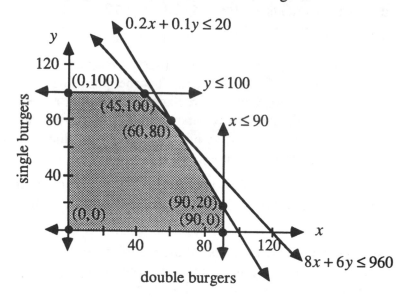

   Since the maximum profit of $110.50 occurs at the corner point (45,100), the restaurant should prepare 45 double burgers and 100 singles for the lunch-time rush.

2. Sample response: Using h for the number of hot dogs, c for the number of bags of chips, and p for the number of cans of pop, the three constraints can be expressed as:

   $$0.15h + 0.2c + 0.35p \leq 108$$
   $$c \leq 2h$$
   $$c + h \leq 3p$$

   The corresponding matrix equation for the boundaries of these constraints is:

   $$\begin{bmatrix} 0.15 & 0.2 & 0.35 \\ -2 & 1 & 0 \\ 1 & 1 & -3 \end{bmatrix} \bullet \begin{bmatrix} h \\ c \\ p \end{bmatrix} = \begin{bmatrix} 108 \\ 0 \\ 0 \end{bmatrix}$$

   The solution to this system is (120,240,120). The profit equation is $P = 0.85h + 0.8c + 0.65p$. At this corner point, the profit is $372.

1. Use inequalities to describe the points graphed on the following number line.

2. Use inequalities to describe the points graphed in the shaded region below.

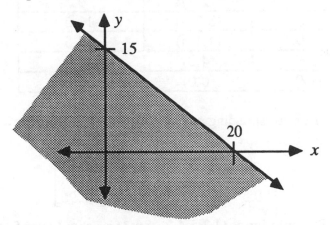

3. Which point in the graph below maximizes the value of the objective function $P = 3x + y$? Defend your response.

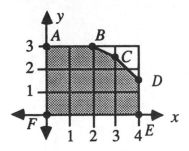

4. Consider the system of linear equations below:

$$2x - 3y + z = 2.7$$
$$4x + 2.4y - 1.5z = 11.7$$
$$\frac{1}{2}x + 9y + 3.8z = 39.96$$

a. Write a matrix equation for this system.

b. Solve the system and verify your solution.

c. Determine the value of the objective function $P = 3x + 2y - 5z$ at the point described in Part **b**.

Answers to Module Assessment

1. $3 < x \le 21$

2. $15x + 20y \le 300$

3. Sample response: According to the corner principle, the maximum value of an objective function occurs at a corner point of the feasible region. As shown in the table below, the maximum of 13.5 occurs at point D.

Point	Coordinates	$P = 3x + y$
A	(0,3)	3
B	(2,3)	9
C	(3,2.5)	11.5
D	(4,1.5)	13.5
E	(4,0)	12
F	(0,0)	0

4.   a. The corresponding matrix equation is shown below:

$$\begin{bmatrix} 2 & -3 & 1 \\ 4 & 2.4 & -1.5 \\ 0.5 & 9 & 3.8 \end{bmatrix} \bullet \begin{bmatrix} x \\ y \\ z \end{bmatrix} = \begin{bmatrix} 2.7 \\ 11.7 \\ 39.96 \end{bmatrix}$$

   b. The solution is (3,2.5,4.2). Students should verify their solutions by substituting into the original equations.

   c. $P = -7$

Flashbacks

Activity 1

1.1 Graph each of the following inequalities on a number line:

    a. $x \leq 25$

    b. $-16 < x$

    c. $-2 \leq x < 4$

1.2 Graph $x \geq -4$ and $y < 7$ on a two-dimensional coordinate system and name three points in the intersecting region.

1.3. Graph $y \geq -4$, $x \leq 0$, and $2x \geq y - 4$ on a two-dimensional coordinate system and name three points in the intersecting region.

1.4 Identify the inequalities whose intersection is the shaded region on the graph below.

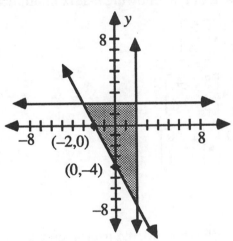

Activity 2

2.1 Identify the slope and y-intercept of the line represented by each of the following equations.

    a. $2y - 4x = 12$

    b. $-y + 16 = 3x$

2.2 Given the equation $w = 3.56a - 4.1b$, find w for each of the following values of a and b:

    a. $a = 2$ and $b = 6$

    b. $a = -5$ and $b = 0$

2.3 Determine the equation, in slope-intercept form, of the line that passes through $(2,4)$ and $(-5,1)$.

Activity 3

3.1 Complete each of the following matrix multiplications.

    a. $\begin{bmatrix} 2 & 7 \\ -3 & 6 \end{bmatrix} \cdot \begin{bmatrix} 5 \\ -1 \end{bmatrix}$

    b. $\begin{bmatrix} 1 & 0 \\ 0 & 1 \end{bmatrix} \cdot \begin{bmatrix} 3 & 4 \\ 2 & -6 \end{bmatrix}$

    c. $\begin{bmatrix} 2 & 11 \\ -7 & 5 \end{bmatrix} \cdot \begin{bmatrix} 1 & 0 \\ 2 & 1 \end{bmatrix}$

Activity 4

4.1 Each of the following ordered triples represents the coordinates of a point in the form (x, y, z). Plot and label each point on a three-dimensional coordinate system.

    a. $(0,3,0)$

    b. $(5,3,2)$

    c. $(8,7,3)$

4.2 Find the points of intersection, if any, for each of the following pairs of lines.

    a. $x + y = 6$ and $y = 4$

    b. $2x - y = 4$ and $x + 3y = -3$

    c. $x = 4 - 2y$ and $y = -3$

Answers to Flashbacks

Activity 1

1.1 **a.** Sample graph:

25

b. Sample graph:

–16

c. Sample graph:

–2   4

1.2 Sample response: Three points in the intersecting region are (0,0), (–4,6.9), and (40,–50).

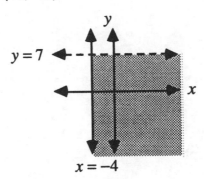

1.3 Sample response: Three points in the intersecting region are: (0,0), (–4,–4), and (–1,–1).

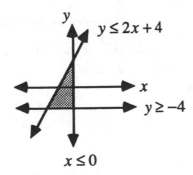

1.4 $y \geq -2x - 4, \ y \leq 2, \ x \leq 2$

Activity 2

2.1   **a.** $m = 2$, $b = 6$

        b. $m = -3$, $b = 16$

2.2   **a.** $w = -17.48$

        b. $w = -17.8$

2.3   Sample response:

$$(y - 4) = \left(\frac{4 - 1}{2 - (-5)}\right)(x - 2)$$

$$y = \frac{3}{7}x - \frac{34}{7}$$

Activity 3

3.1   **a.** $\begin{bmatrix} 3 \\ -21 \end{bmatrix}$

        b. $\begin{bmatrix} 3 & 4 \\ 2 & -6 \end{bmatrix}$

        c. $\begin{bmatrix} 24 & 11 \\ 3 & 5 \end{bmatrix}$

Activity 4

4.1   **a.** Sample graph:

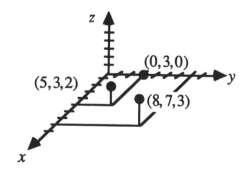

4.2   **a.** $(2,4)$

        b. $\left(\frac{9}{7}, \frac{-10}{7}\right)$

        c. $(10, -3)$

Crazy Cartoons

How are cartoon characters made? How do they change shape? How can you make an inanimate object appear to move? A cartoonist—or a math student—can help answer these questions.

Monty Brekke • *John Carter* • *Janet Kuchenbrod*

Crazy Cartoons

Overview

Students explore transformations in a plane, including dilations, translations, rotations, reflections, and composite transformations.

Objectives

In this module, students will:

- use the properties of similar figures
- calculate distances between points in the Cartesian plane
- explore the geometric relationships in perspective drawings, dilations centered at the origin, translations, rotations about the origin, reflections, and composite transformations
- write matrices for dilations centered at the origin, translations, rotations about the origin, and reflections
- use matrix equations to transform geometric figures on the Cartesian plane.

Prerequisites

For this module, students should know:

- how to graph points in the Cartesian plane
- the relationships between similar figures
- how to solve systems of linear equations
- how to perform operations on matrices, including scalar multiplication, matrix addition, and matrix multiplication
- how to find the equation of a line given two points on the line
- how to use trigonometric ratios to determine angle measures
- how to reflect a set of points in a line.

Time Line

Activity	1	2	3	4	5	Summary Assessment	Total
Days	3	2	2	2	2	1	12

Teacher Note

Students may use graph paper, tracing paper, MIRAs™, transparent grids, graphing calculators, spreadsheets, or other appropriate graphing utilities to perform transformations. In addition, you may want to use technology to solve matrix equations or simultaneous equations.

Materials Required

Materials	Activity					
	1	2	3	4	5	Summary Assessment
rulers	X	X	X	X	X	X
graph paper	X	X	X	X	X	X
protractors	X			X		X
template for Problem 2.7		X				
tracing paper		X	X	X	X	X
decks of playing cards				X		

Teacher Note

A blackline master of the template appears at the end of this teacher edition.

Technology

Software	Activity					
	1	2	3	4	5	Summary Assessment
geometry utility	X		X		X	X
graphing utility	X	X	X	X		X
spreadsheet		X	X	X	X	X
matrix manipulator		X	X	X	X	X

Crazy Cartoons

Introduction (page 209)

Students describe transformations in general terms, without the use of coordinates.

Discussion (page 209)

a. Sample response: The bug in frame B is a reflection of the bug in frame A with respect to a vertical line. The bug in frame C is a 60° clockwise rotation of the bug in frame A. The bug in frame D is a 90° counterclockwise rotation of the bug in frame A. The bug in frame E is a scaled-down version of the bug in frame A. The bug in frame F is a scaled-up version of the bug in frame A.

b. Sample response: The bug in frame B can be described as the combination of a 180° rotation of the bug in frame A, followed by a reflection with respect to a horizontal line.

(page 210)

Activity 1

In this activity, students explore dilations by graphing shapes in the coordinate plane. They create and measure similar shapes using a geometry utility.

Materials List

- graph paper (one sheet per student)
- rulers (one per student)
- protractors (one per student)

Technology

- geometry utility

Teacher Note

Point of perspective and dilations are important in both drawing and painting. You may wish to use one or both of the following quotations to initiate a class discussion.

- The optical model, or the visual pyramid, can secure the correctness of the painter's representation of reality. The painting . . . should be conceived as a "planar representation" of the visual pyramid. All the figures, objects, and spatial distances painted on the artist's panel are fully proportional to those found in the actual world that the painting represents. Perspective construction, then, makes it provable that a picture is "correct" in its rendering of space. (Barasch, *Theories of Art*)

- . . . perspective construction begins with a series of arbitrary acts, as the painter selects a visual field of "whatever size I want," picks a size for the human figures, and places his centric point "wherever I wish." (Hulse, *The Rule of Art*)

Exploration   (page 211)

a–b.   Sample graph:

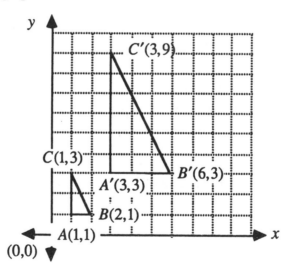

c.   In the following sample table, lengths are measured in centimeters and angles are measured in degrees.

Preimage		Image	
AB	1	$A'B'$	3
BC	$\sqrt{5} \approx 2.2$	$B'C'$	$3\sqrt{5} \approx 6.6$
CA	2	$C'A'$	6
$m\angle ABC$	63°	$m\angle A'B'C'$	63°
$m\angle BCA$	27°	$m\angle B'C'A'$	27°
$m\angle CAB$	90°	$m\angle C'A'B'$	90°

264

d.   The ratios of corresponding lengths are 3/1.

e.   Sample graph:

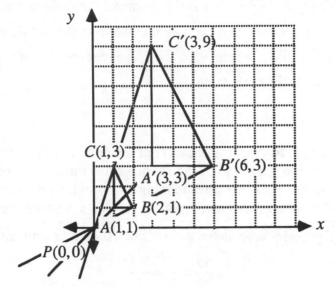

f. $PA = \sqrt{2} \approx 1.4$, $PB = \sqrt{5} \approx 2.2$, $PC = \sqrt{10} \approx 3.2$, $PA' = 3\sqrt{2} \approx 4.2$, $PB' = 3\sqrt{5} \approx 6.6$, $PC' = 3\sqrt{10} \approx 9.5$

g–h.   As in Part **d**, the ratios of corresponding lengths are 3/1.

Discussion

(page 212)

a.   Sample response: The segment connecting two points can be thought of as the hypotenuse of a right triangle. The length of the horizontal side is $|x_2 - x_1|$ and the length of the vertical side is $|y_2 - y_1|$. Using the Pythagorean theorem, the distance d between the two points is:

$$d^2 = (x_2 - x_1)^2 + (y_2 - y_1)^2$$
$$d = \sqrt{(x_2 - x_1)^2 + (y_2 - y_1)^2}$$

b.   The ratios of corresponding lengths are equal.

c.   Sample response: The point of perspective is the center of dilation. The resulting figures are similar.

d.   The corresponding angles are congruent.

e.   In a dilation, the corresponding lengths are proportional and the corresponding angles are congruent.

f.   **1.** $\triangle ABC \sim \triangle A'B'C'$

        2. $\triangle PAC \sim \triangle P'A'C'$, $\triangle PAB \sim \triangle P'A'B'$, and $\triangle PBC \sim \triangle P'B'C'$

265

g. **1.** The scale factor equals the ratio of corresponding lengths.

2. The scale factor equals the ratio of perimeters.

3. The ratio of the areas is the square of the scale factor.

h. Sample response: Yes, because the two triangles would still be similar.

i. A scale factor *x*, where $-1 < x < 1$, reduces the size of the original shape.

j. The ratio is the scale factor.

Assignment (page 214)

1.1 **a.** Sample response: The center of the dilation can be found by drawing a line through *A* and *A'* and another line through *C* and *C'* (or through any two pairs of corresponding points in the image and the preimage). The point of intersection of the two lines is the center of dilation.

b. The scale factor is the ratio of corresponding lengths:

$$\frac{55}{22} = \frac{5}{2} = \frac{2.5}{1}$$

1.2 Sample response: No. The figures are not similar; therefore, they could not have been produced by a dilation. There is no point of perspective.

1.3 **a–c.** Sample graph:

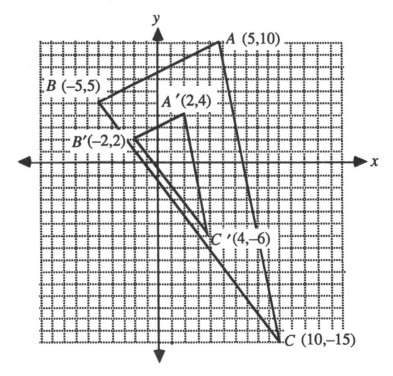

d. **1.** 2

2. −1/5

3. 2.5

266

1.4   **a.** Sample graph:

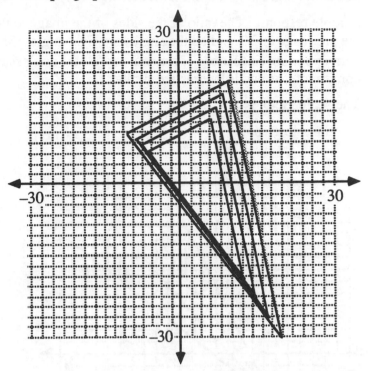

b. Sample response: The triangle would appear to double in size, growing like an animated cartoon.

c. Sample response: Assign one figure to represent the preimage and the other to represent the image. Using the origin as the center of dilation, dilate the preimage by a scale factor equivalent to the ratio of the corresponding lengths of the image to the preimage.

*1.5   **a.** 3/1

b. 1/2

c. 3/2

d. Sample response: They could not have the same center. When you draw lines through corresponding points in the images and preimages, they do not intersect at the same point.

* * * * *

1.6   The center of dilation is the origin and the scale factor is 2/1.

1.7   Sketches will vary. Students should record the coordinates of the point of perspective (which is also the center of dilation). They should also describe how the coordinates of an image point X' and its preimage X can be used to find the scale factor r as follows:

$$r = \frac{PX'}{PX}$$

267

1.8   **a.** See sample graph given in Part **d** below.

  b. Sample response: The ratio of the sides of the image to the sides of the preimage is 2/1 and all the angles are right angles. Since the corresponding sides are proportional and all the angles are congruent, the quadrilaterals are similar.

  c. The scale factor is 2.

  d. **1.** Sample graph:

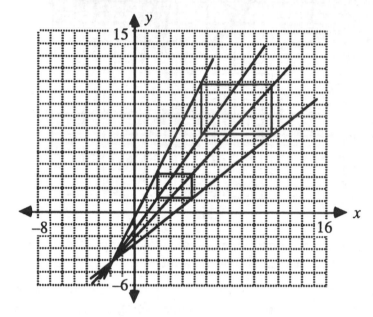

  2. Sample response: The coordinates of the point of perspective are approximately (–2,–4).

  3. Sample response: The equation of the line containing A' and A is:

$$y - 1.2 = \left(\frac{6.7 - 1.2}{5.3 - 1.9}\right) \cdot (x - 1.9)$$

$$y = \frac{55}{34}x - \frac{637}{340}$$

The equation of the line containing B' and B is:

$$y - 1.2 = \left(\frac{6.7 - 1.2}{11.3 - 4.9}\right) \cdot (x - 4.9)$$

$$y = \frac{55}{64}x - \frac{1927}{640}$$

Their point of intersection is (–1.5,–4.3).

* * * * * * * * *

268

Activity 2

In this activity, students use matrices to store the coordinates of points that define a figure. They discover that a dilation with center at the origin can be represented by scalar multiplication of the matrix or by a multiplication on the left by a 2×2 matrix.

Materials List

- graph paper (one sheet per student)

- ruler (one per student)

- tracing paper (one sheet per student)

- template for Problem **2.7** (one per student; a blackline master appears at the end of this teacher edition)

Technology

- matrix manipulator

- spreadsheet

- graphing utility

Teacher Note

When using some types of technology (such as spreadsheets, for example) to draw closed figures, it may be necessary to repeat the coordinates of some points in a matrix. For example, a triangle can be defined on a coordinate grid by listing the coordinates of three points (the three vertices) in a 2×3 matrix. However, in order to use a spreadsheet to draw the same triangle from a matrix, it may be necessary to list the coordinates of both a starting point and a stopping point (or four points in all).

Alternately, students may simply use the spreadsheet utility to print an unconnected scatterplot, then connect the points by hand.

Exploration

(page 217)

In this exploration, students draw and transform Skip on a coordinate plane.

a.   Sample graph:

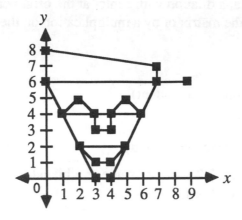

b.   Sample matrix:

$$M = \begin{bmatrix} 2 & 5 & 4 & 3 \\ 2 & 2 & 1 & 1 \end{bmatrix}$$

c.   Sample graph:

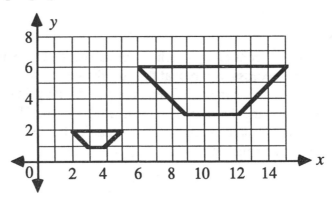

d.   Sample matrix:

$$M' = \begin{bmatrix} 6 & 15 & 12 & 9 \\ 6 & 6 & 3 & 3 \end{bmatrix}$$

270

e. Students may use the following matrix equation to create eight equations with four unknowns.

$$\mathbf{D \bullet M = M'}$$

$$\begin{bmatrix} a & b \\ c & d \end{bmatrix} \bullet \begin{bmatrix} 2 & 5 & 4 & 3 \\ 2 & 2 & 1 & 1 \end{bmatrix} = \begin{bmatrix} 6 & 15 & 12 & 9 \\ 6 & 6 & 3 & 3 \end{bmatrix}$$

$$\begin{bmatrix} 2a+2b & 5a+2b & 4a+1b & 3a+1b \\ 2c+2d & 5c+2d & 4c+1d & 3c+1d \end{bmatrix} = \begin{bmatrix} 6 & 15 & 12 & 9 \\ 6 & 6 & 3 & 3 \end{bmatrix}$$

By solving this system of equations, students can determine the elements of **D**.

$$\begin{array}{ll} 2a+2b = 6 & 2c+2d = 6 \\ 5a+2b = 15 & 5c+2d = 6 \\ 4a+1b = 12 & 4c+1d = 3 \\ 3a+1b = 9 & 3c+1d = 3 \end{array} \Rightarrow \mathbf{D} = \begin{bmatrix} 3 & 0 \\ 0 & 3 \end{bmatrix}$$

f. Skip can be drawn without lifting a pencil or retracing a segment using the circuit shown below. Because Skip can be drawn with a circuit, students can use a spreadsheet to graph the cartoon without adding additional, unwanted segments. **Note:** There are several other ways to trace through the figure. Only one possibility is shown here.

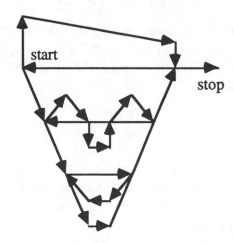

In the following sample matrix, the coordinates of some points have been repeated in order to obtain the graph of a closed figure.

$$\mathbf{S} = \begin{bmatrix} 0 & 0 & 7 & 7 & 0 & 1 & 2 & 3 & 3 & 4 & 4 & 5 & 6 & 1 & 2 & 5 & 4 & 3 & 2 & 3 & 4 & 7 & 9 \\ 6 & 8 & 7 & 6 & 6 & 4 & 5 & 4 & 3 & 3 & 4 & 5 & 4 & 4 & 2 & 2 & 1 & 1 & 2 & 0 & 0 & 6 & 6 \end{bmatrix}$$

g. The elements in matrix **S′** are three times greater than the corresponding elements in matrix **S**.

271

Discussion

a. Sample response: A dilation by a scale factor of 3, with center at the origin, can be accomplished by multiplying the preimage matrix by the scalar 3 to obtain the image matrix.

b. In order to multiply matrices, the number of columns in the matrix on the left must equal the number of rows in the matrix on the right.

c. 1. $\begin{bmatrix} 3 & 0 \\ 0 & 3 \end{bmatrix}$

2. $\begin{bmatrix} 1/4 & 0 \\ 0 & 1/4 \end{bmatrix}$

3. $\begin{bmatrix} 1 & 0 \\ 0 & 1 \end{bmatrix}$

d. As shown in the following equation, when an identity matrix is multiplied by a scalar k, the product is the transformation matrix for a dilation of scale factor k, with center at the origin.

$$k \bullet \begin{bmatrix} 1 & 0 \\ 0 & 1 \end{bmatrix} = \begin{bmatrix} k & 0 \\ 0 & k \end{bmatrix}$$

e. Sample response: To determine the matrix that represents the image of Skip, you could multiply each entry by n, multiply the matrix that represents Skip's face by a scalar of n, or multiply on the left by the following matrix:

$$\begin{bmatrix} n & 0 \\ 0 & n \end{bmatrix}$$

e. Sample response: In a dilation, the image and preimage are similar. They have the same shape and their corresponding angles are congruent. The lengths of the sides of the image are proportional to those of the preimage.

Teacher Note

To complete Problem **2.7**, each student will require a copy of the template. A blackline master appears at the end of this teacher edition.

2.1 **a.** Answers may vary. Sample matrix:

$$\mathbf{P} = \begin{bmatrix} 0 & 2 & 5 & 6 & 3 & 0 \\ 3 & 7 & 5 & 2 & 0 & 3 \end{bmatrix}$$

  b. 1. Sample response using scalar multiplication:

$$\mathbf{P}' = 3.5 \cdot \begin{bmatrix} 0 & 2 & 5 & 6 & 3 & 0 \\ 3 & 7 & 5 & 2 & 0 & 3 \end{bmatrix}$$

  2. Sample response using multiplication by a 2×2 matrix:

$$\mathbf{P}' = \begin{bmatrix} 3.5 & 0 \\ 0 & 3.5 \end{bmatrix} \cdot \begin{bmatrix} 0 & 2 & 5 & 6 & 3 & 0 \\ 3 & 7 & 5 & 2 & 0 & 3 \end{bmatrix}$$

  c. Sample matrix:

$$\mathbf{P}' = \begin{bmatrix} 0 & 7 & 17.5 & 21 & 10.5 & 0 \\ 10.5 & 24.5 & 17.5 & 7 & 0 & 10.5 \end{bmatrix}$$

2.2 **a.** Sample response: $5 \cdot \mathbf{S} = \mathbf{S}'$ or

$$\begin{bmatrix} 5 & 0 \\ 0 & 5 \end{bmatrix} \cdot \mathbf{S} = \mathbf{S}'$$

  b. Sample response:

$$\mathbf{C}' = 0.75 \cdot \begin{bmatrix} 9 & 0 & 0 & 7 & 7 \\ 6 & 6 & 8 & 7 & 6 \end{bmatrix}$$

  c. Using matrix **M** from Part **b** of the exploration,

$$\mathbf{M} = \begin{bmatrix} 2 & 5 & 4 & 3 \\ 2 & 2 & 1 & 1 \end{bmatrix}$$

then the coordinates for the image of Skip's mouth under the given dilation are represented in the following matrix:

$$\mathbf{M}' = \begin{bmatrix} 1.5 & 3.75 & 3 & 2.25 \\ 1.5 & 1.5 & 0.75 & 0.75 \end{bmatrix}$$

*2.3 **a.** Sample matrix:

$$\mathbf{B} = \begin{bmatrix} a & i & g & e & c \\ b & j & h & f & d \end{bmatrix}$$

  b. The scale factor from B to A is 1/2 or 0.5. The scale factor from B to C is 3/1.

273

c. Sample response:

$$A = 0.5 \cdot B$$

$$= \begin{bmatrix} 0.5a & 0.5i & 0.5g & 0.5e & 0.5c \\ 0.5b & 0.5j & 0.5h & 0.5f & 0.5d \end{bmatrix}$$

d. Sample response:

$$C = \begin{bmatrix} 6 & 0 \\ 0 & 6 \end{bmatrix} \cdot \begin{bmatrix} 0.5a & 0.5i & 0.5g & 0.5e & 0.5c \\ 0.5b & 0.5j & 0.5h & 0.5f & 0.5d \end{bmatrix}$$

$$= \begin{bmatrix} 3a & 3i & 3g & 3e & 3c \\ 3b & 3j & 3h & 3f & 3d \end{bmatrix}$$

*2.4 The dilation of Skip by a scale factor of 3 with center at the origin can be accomplished using the matrix operation $3 \cdot S = S'$, where S is the matrix representation for Skip and S' is the matrix representation for Skip's image. Sample graph:

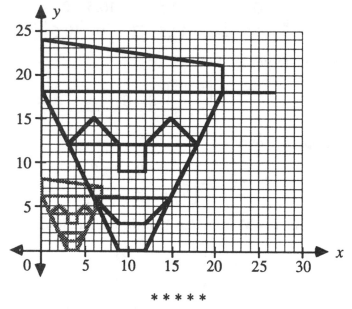

* * * * *

2.5 Sample response:

	small	medium	large	x-large
blue	120	280	120	160
red	200	320	80	40

2.6 **a.** Sample response: At 6:00 p.m. on Tuesday, the diameter of the earth's image appears to be about 0.8 cm. At 1:00 a.m. on Wednesday, the diameter of the earth's image appears to be about 2.3 cm. The scale factor is about $2.3/0.8 \approx 2.9$.

b. Sample response: After another 7 hr, the diameter of the earth's image should appear to be about 6.7 cm, which is 2.9 times larger than 2.3 cm.

274

2.7 **a.** As shown in the diagram below, the position of the flashlight can be determined by drawing the lines that connect corresponding vertices.

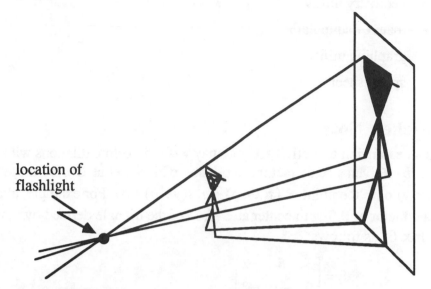

location of flashlight

b. Sample response: Chip should hold the flashlight so that its distance from the wall is five times its distance from Skip. Then the ratio PX'/PX, or the scale factor, will equal 5.

c. Sample response: As Chip moves the flashlight toward Skip, his shadow will grow larger. This is because the ratio of the distance from the flashlight to the wall to the distance from the flashlight to Skip becomes larger.

* * * * * * * * * *

(page 222)

Activity 3

In this activity, students explore translations in the coordinate plane.

Materials List
- graph paper
- tracing paper
- ruler (one per student)

Technology

- geometry utility
- matrix manipulator
- graphing utility
- spreadsheet

Teacher Note

As an extension to Activity **3**, you may wish to explore dilations with center at $C(a,b)$. Given a scale factor s, a dilation with center at $C(a,b)$ maps the point $P(x,y)$ onto the point $P'(s(x-a)+a, s(y-b)+b)$. For example, a dilation by a scale factor of 0.5 with center at $C(5,6)$ of the triangle defined by matrix **S** yields matrix **S**′ as follows:

$$\mathbf{S} = \begin{bmatrix} 3 & 5 & -2 \\ 6 & -1 & -3 \end{bmatrix}$$

$$\mathbf{S}' = \begin{bmatrix} 0.5(3-5)+5 & 0.5(5-5)+5 & 0.5(-2-5)+5 \\ 0.5(6-6)+6 & 0.5(-1-6)+6 & 0.5(-3-6)+6 \end{bmatrix}$$

$$\mathbf{S}' = \begin{bmatrix} 4 & 5 & 1.5 \\ 6 & 2.5 & 1.5 \end{bmatrix}$$

Exploration

(page 222)

a.   **1–2.** Students trace Skip's movements through the translation vector, then through this vector's vertical and horizontal components. In both cases, Skip's image moves to the same position at the bottom of the slide.

b.   Sample graph:

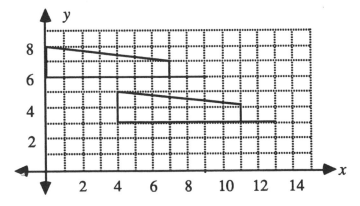

c.   Students should observe that every x-value in matrix **C** is increased by 4 and every y-value is decreased by 3.

276

d–e. Students should write and verify the following equation:

$$C + T = C'$$

$$\begin{bmatrix} 9 & 0 & 0 & 7 & 7 \\ 6 & 6 & 8 & 7 & 6 \end{bmatrix} + \begin{bmatrix} 4 & 4 & 4 & 4 & 4 \\ -3 & -3 & -3 & -3 & -3 \end{bmatrix} = \begin{bmatrix} 13 & 4 & 4 & 11 & 11 \\ 3 & 3 & 5 & 4 & 3 \end{bmatrix}$$

Discussion

a. Sample response: The two images coincided.

b. Skip's preimage and image are congruent.

c. Sample response: The image has been moved 4 units to the right and 3 units down from the preimage.

d. The following matrix translates the seven points matrix **C** 5 units down and 4 units to the left.

$$\mathbf{T}_{C,C'} = \begin{bmatrix} -4 & -4 & -4 & -4 & -4 & -4 \\ -5 & -5 & -5 & -5 & -5 & -5 \end{bmatrix}$$

e. Sample response: Since the translation vector and its vertical and horizontal components form a right triangle, you could find the length of the translation vector using the Pythagorean theorem.

f. Sample response: To find the measure of the angle between the vertical component and the translation vector, you could use the inverse tangent.

g. Sample response: The distance between a point in the preimage and the corresponding point in the image is the length of the translation vector.

h. 1. Using the distance formula, the length of the translation vector is
$$\sqrt{(x + h - x)^2 + (y + k - y)^2} = \sqrt{h^2 + k^2}.$$

2. Sample response: The angle between the horizontal component and the translation vector is $\tan^{-1}(k/h)$.

Assignment

3.1 Sample response: Skip was translated 5 units in a direction approximately 37° measured counterclockwise from the horizontal.

3.2 **a.** Sample matrix equation:

$$\begin{bmatrix} 1 & 5 & 4 & 0 \\ 1 & 1 & 4 & 4 \end{bmatrix} + \begin{bmatrix} 4 & 4 & 4 & 4 \\ -2 & -2 & -2 & -2 \end{bmatrix} = \begin{bmatrix} 5 & 9 & 8 & 4 \\ -1 & -1 & 2 & 2 \end{bmatrix}$$

b. Sample graph:

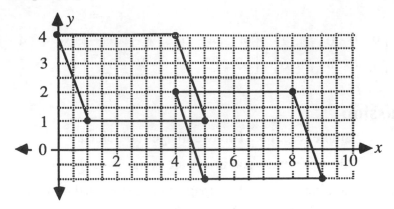

3.3   **a.** Sample response: The matrix consists of five columns and two rows. Each entry in the first row is 7, to represent the horizontal movement. Each entry in the second row is –6, to represent the vertical movement.

      b. Sample matrix equation:

$$\begin{bmatrix} 1 & 2 & 3 & 4 & 5 \\ 1 & 6 & 4 & 6 & 1 \end{bmatrix} + \begin{bmatrix} 7 & 7 & 7 & 7 & 7 \\ -6 & -6 & -6 & -6 & -6 \end{bmatrix} = \begin{bmatrix} 8 & 9 & 10 & 11 & 12 \\ -5 & 0 & -2 & 0 & -5 \end{bmatrix}$$

      c. The measure of the angle is approximately 49.4°.

      d. The length of the translation vector can be found as follows:
$$\sqrt{(8-1)^2 + (-5-1)^2} = \sqrt{49+36} = \sqrt{85} \approx 9.22.$$

3.4   **a.** See diagram given in Problem **3.3** (student edition).

      b. Sample response: As you flipped through the cards, the M would appear to move down the page. **Note:** You may wish to allow students to actually create the flip cards. If so, the origin must be in the same position on each card, and each drawing must be taped in the appropriate location relative to the origin.

      c. Sample response: Create a transformation matrix by subtracting the row and column values in the preimage matrix from the corresponding values in the image matrix. Then multiply this matrix by $1/n$, where n is the total number of images desired.

*3.5   **a.** Since students choose their own translations, answers will vary. In each translation matrix, both h and k should be less than 0.

      b. To obtain the image matrix S', h is added to each element in row 1 and k is added to each element in row 2.

*3.6 **a. 1.** Sample equation for the translation:

$$\begin{bmatrix} 3 & 2 & -1 & -2 & -1 & 2 \\ 1 & 7 & 7 & 1 & -4 & -4 \end{bmatrix} + \begin{bmatrix} 3 & 3 & 3 & 3 & 3 & 3 \\ -8 & -8 & -8 & -8 & -8 & -8 \end{bmatrix} =$$

$$\begin{bmatrix} 6 & 5 & 2 & 1 & 2 & 5 \\ -7 & -1 & -1 & -7 & -12 & -12 \end{bmatrix}$$

Sample equation for the dilation:

$$2 \cdot \begin{bmatrix} 6 & 5 & 2 & 1 & 2 & 5 \\ -7 & -1 & -1 & -7 & -12 & -12 \end{bmatrix} =$$

$$\begin{bmatrix} 12 & 10 & 4 & 2 & 4 & 10 \\ -14 & -2 & -2 & -14 & -24 & -24 \end{bmatrix}$$

2. The final image has vertices at (12,–14), (10,–2), (4,–2), (2,–14), (4,–24), and (10,–24). Sample graph:

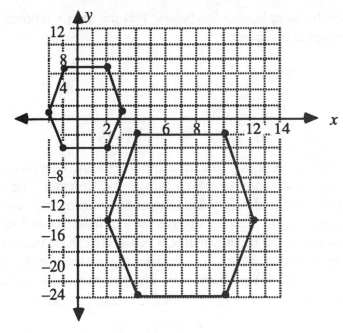

3. In the sample equation below, **P** is the matrix representation of the original preimage:

$$2 \cdot \left[\mathbf{P} + \begin{bmatrix} 3 & 3 & 3 & 3 & 3 & 3 \\ -8 & -8 & -8 & -8 & -8 & -8 \end{bmatrix} \right] =$$

$$\begin{bmatrix} 12 & 10 & 4 & 2 & 4 & 10 \\ -14 & -2 & -2 & -14 & -24 & -24 \end{bmatrix}$$

b. The final image has vertices at (9,–6), (7,6), (1,6), (–1,–6), (1,–16), and (7,–16). Sample graph:

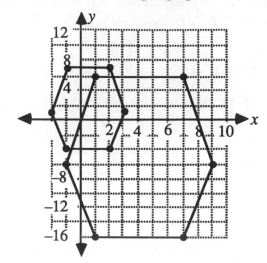

In the sample equation below, **P** is the matrix representation of the original preimage:

$$2 \cdot \mathbf{P} + \begin{bmatrix} 3 & 3 & 3 & 3 & 3 & 3 \\ -8 & -8 & -8 & -8 & -8 & -8 \end{bmatrix}$$

$$= \begin{bmatrix} 9 & 7 & 1 & -1 & 1 & 7 \\ -6 & 6 & 6 & -6 & -16 & -16 \end{bmatrix}$$

c. Sample response: The transformations are not equivalent. The two figures are congruent but positioned differently. The image in Part **a** is 3 units to the right and 8 units down from the image in Part **b**. In other words, it seems to have been translated one additional time. **Note:** It can be shown algebraically that these two composite transformations are not equivalent using the distributive property of multiplication over addition. The transformation in Part **a** is $2(P+T) = 2P + 2T$; the transformation in Part **b** is $2P + T$.

★ ★ ★ ★ ★

3.7   **a.** Sample response: In this translation, the image of quadrilateral *ABCD* moves 8 units to the right and 2 units up.

b. $\begin{bmatrix} 8 & 8 & 8 & 8 \\ 2 & 2 & 2 & 2 \end{bmatrix}$

c. The distance between each point X and its image X' is $\sqrt{8^2 + 2^2} = \sqrt{68} \approx 8.25$.

3.8   **a.** The coordinates are $A''(0,2)$, $B''(-6,4)$, and $C''(-1,-4)$.

b. **1.** In this translation, the image of triangle ABC moves 2 units to the left and 2 units down.

2. $\begin{bmatrix} -2 & -2 & -2 \\ -2 & -2 & -2 \end{bmatrix}$

c. The distance between each point X and its image X' is
$$\sqrt{(-2)^2 + (-2)^2} = \sqrt{8} \approx 2.83.$$

* * * * * * * * * *

(page 227)

Activity 4

Students investigate rotations about the origin for specific degree measures.

Materials List

- graph paper (one sheet per student)
- ruler (one per student)
- protractor (one per student)
- tracing paper (one sheet per student)
- standard deck of playing cards (for Problem **4.10**)

Technology

- matrix manipulator
- graphing utility
- spreadsheet

Exploration   (page 227)

Students develop the transformation matrices for 180°, 360°, and 90° rotations.

a–b. By rotating the tracing paper 180° counterclockwise about the origin, students should be able to estimate the coordinates for the image matrix of Chip's mouth. Sample matrix:

$$\mathbf{P'} = \begin{bmatrix} -2 & -4 & -6 \\ -2 & 0 & -2 \end{bmatrix}$$

281

c. Sample response: The matrix of the image formed by a 180° counterclockwise rotation can be found by multiplying the matrix of the preimage by the scalar –1.

d. When multiplied on the left of a matrix of ordered pairs, the matrix below produces a 180° rotation about the origin:

$$\begin{bmatrix} -1 & 0 \\ 0 & -1 \end{bmatrix}$$

e. **1.** By rotating the tracing paper 360° counterclockwise about the origin, students should be able to estimate the coordinates for the following image matrix:

$$P' = \begin{bmatrix} 2 & 4 & 6 \\ 2 & 0 & 2 \end{bmatrix}$$

Students may conjecture that multiplication by the scalar 1 is required for a 360° counterclockwise rotation. When multiplied on the left of a matrix of ordered pairs, the matrix below produces a 180° rotation about the origin:

$$\begin{bmatrix} 1 & 0 \\ 0 & 1 \end{bmatrix}$$

2. By rotating the tracing paper 90° counterclockwise about the origin, students should be able to estimate the coordinates for the following image matrix:

$$P' = \begin{bmatrix} -2 & 0 & -2 \\ 2 & 4 & 6 \end{bmatrix}$$

When multiplied on the left of a matrix of ordered pairs, the matrix below produces a 90° counterclockwise rotation about the origin:

$$\begin{bmatrix} 0 & -1 \\ 1 & 0 \end{bmatrix}$$

Discussion   (page 228)

a. Sample response: The image would be the same as the preimage.

b. Sample response: Since multiplication by the identity matrix would not change the preimage matrix, it could be thought of as producing a 0° rotation about the origin.

c. In general, a rotation about the origin of any multiple of 360° will produce the same result as a rotation of 360°.

d. A clockwise rotation of 270° produces the same image as a counterclockwise rotation of 90°. In general, a clockwise rotation of $k°$ is equivalent to a counterclockwise rotation of $(n \cdot 360° - k)$ for any integer n.

e. Sample response: Yes. Since the end result is the same, the rotations are equivalent.

f. In a rotation, the image and the preimage are congruent.

Assignment

(page 229)

4.1 **a. 1.** The image matrix is the same as matrix **M**.

2. $M' = \begin{bmatrix} -2 & -5 & -4 & -3 \\ -2 & -2 & -1 & -1 \end{bmatrix}$

3. $M' = \begin{bmatrix} -2 & -2 & -1 & -1 \\ 2 & 5 & 4 & 3 \end{bmatrix}$

b. Sample graph:

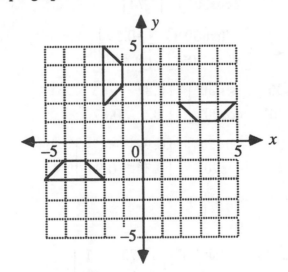

*4.2 **a.** The image matrix for Skip's mouth under a 270° counterclockwise rotation about the origin is:

$$M' = \begin{bmatrix} -2 & -2 & -1 & -1 \\ 2 & 5 & 4 & 3 \end{bmatrix}$$

b. When multiplied on the left of a matrix of ordered pairs, the following matrix produces a 270° rotation about the origin:

$$\begin{bmatrix} 0 & 1 \\ -1 & 0 \end{bmatrix}$$

4.3 **a.** **1.** $a = \cos 30° \approx 0.87$

2. $b = \sin 30° = 0.5$

3. $\mathbf{P}' = \begin{bmatrix} \cos 30° \\ \sin 30° \end{bmatrix} \approx \begin{bmatrix} 0.87 \\ 0.5 \end{bmatrix}$

b. **1.** $\mathbf{P}' = \begin{bmatrix} 2\cos 30° \\ 2\sin 30° \end{bmatrix} \approx \begin{bmatrix} 1.73 \\ 1 \end{bmatrix}$

2. $\mathbf{P}' = \begin{bmatrix} c(\cos 30°) \\ c(\sin 30°) \end{bmatrix} \approx \begin{bmatrix} 0.87c \\ 0.5c \end{bmatrix}$

4.4 **a.** **1.** $a = \sin 30° = 0.5$

2. $b = \cos 30° \approx 0.87$

3. $\mathbf{Q}' = \begin{bmatrix} -\sin 30° \\ \cos 30° \end{bmatrix} \approx \begin{bmatrix} -0.5 \\ 0.87 \end{bmatrix}$

b. **1.** $\mathbf{Q}' = \begin{bmatrix} -2\sin 30° \\ 2\cos 30° \end{bmatrix} \approx \begin{bmatrix} -1 \\ 1.73 \end{bmatrix}$

2. $\mathbf{Q}' = \begin{bmatrix} -d(\sin 30°) \\ d(\cos 30°) \end{bmatrix} \approx \begin{bmatrix} -0.5d \\ 0.87d \end{bmatrix}$

4.5 **a.** $\begin{bmatrix} \cos 30° & -\sin 30° \\ \sin 30° & \cos 30° \end{bmatrix} \approx \begin{bmatrix} 0.87 & -0.5 \\ 0.5 & 0.87 \end{bmatrix}$

b. $\begin{bmatrix} \cos 20° & -\sin 20° \\ \sin 20° & \cos 20° \end{bmatrix} \approx \begin{bmatrix} 0.94 & -0.34 \\ 0.34 & 0.94 \end{bmatrix}$

c. $\begin{bmatrix} \cos n° & -\sin n° \\ \sin n° & \cos n° \end{bmatrix}$

4.6 **a.** $\begin{bmatrix} 2\cos 30° & -2\sin 30° \\ 2\sin 30° & 2\cos 30° \end{bmatrix} \approx \begin{bmatrix} 1.73 & -1 \\ 1 & 1.73 \end{bmatrix}$

b. **1.** $\begin{bmatrix} c(\cos 30°) & -c(\sin 30°) \\ c(\sin 30°) & c(\cos 30°) \end{bmatrix} \approx \begin{bmatrix} 0.87c & -0.5c \\ 0.5c & 0.87c \end{bmatrix}$

2. $\begin{bmatrix} c(\cos n°) & -c(\sin n°) \\ c(\sin n°) & c(\cos n°) \end{bmatrix}$

4.7 Answers will vary, since students choose their own angles of rotation. The following sample equation summarizes a 90° rotation about the origin of Skip's cap:

$$\begin{bmatrix} 0 & -1 \\ 1 & 0 \end{bmatrix} \cdot \begin{bmatrix} 9 & 7 & 0 & 0 & 7 & 7 \\ 6 & 6 & 6 & 8 & 7 & 6 \end{bmatrix} = \begin{bmatrix} -6 & -6 & -6 & -8 & -7 & -6 \\ 9 & 7 & 0 & 0 & 7 & 7 \end{bmatrix}$$

4.8 **a.** $\begin{bmatrix} -1 & 0 \\ 0 & -1 \end{bmatrix} \cdot \begin{bmatrix} 5 & 0 & 0 \\ 0 & 8 & 2 \end{bmatrix} = \begin{bmatrix} -5 & 0 & 0 \\ 0 & -8 & -2 \end{bmatrix}$

b. $\begin{bmatrix} 0 & -1 \\ 1 & 0 \end{bmatrix} \cdot \begin{bmatrix} 5 & 0 & 0 \\ 0 & 8 & 2 \end{bmatrix} = \begin{bmatrix} 0 & -8 & -2 \\ 5 & 0 & 0 \end{bmatrix}$

4.9 Sample response: For each of the following rotations about O, each point in the image coincides with the preimage: 240°, 360°, 0°, −120°, or −240°.

4.10 Answers will vary, depending on the particular design of the cards.

4.11 Sample response: Skip's face does not have rotational symmetry. There is no point about which the face can be rotated to produce an image that coincides with the preimage.

*4.12 **a.** Sample response: A square has rotational symmetry of 90° about its center.

b. a regular octagon

c. 1. 60°

2. 72°

3. 36°

4. 360°/n

* * * * *

285

4.13 **a.** **1.** $S' = \begin{bmatrix} 0 & -4 & 0 & 2 & -2 & 4 \\ -3.4 & -3.4 & 3.4 & 0 & 0 & -3.4 \end{bmatrix}$

  2. $S' = \begin{bmatrix} 3.4 & 3.4 & -3.4 & 0 & 0 & 3.4 \\ 0 & -4 & 0 & 2 & -2 & 4 \end{bmatrix}$

  3. $S' = \begin{bmatrix} 0 & 4 & 0 & -2 & 2 & -4 \\ 3.4 & 3.4 & -3.4 & 0 & 0 & 3.4 \end{bmatrix}$

  4. $S' = \begin{bmatrix} 0 & 4 & 0 & -2 & 2 & -4 \\ 3.4 & 3.4 & -3.4 & 0 & 0 & 3.4 \end{bmatrix}$

  5. $S' = \begin{bmatrix} -3.4 & -3.4 & 3.4 & 0 & 0 & -3.4 \\ 0 & 4 & 0 & -2 & 2 & -4 \end{bmatrix}$

  b. Sample response: The angles which give rotational symmetry about the center are 120° and 240°.

4.14 Sample response: A 90° rotation about the origin takes all points in the first quadrant to points in the second quadrant.

* * * * * * * * * *

(page 234)

Activity 5

In this activity, students examine reflections in the coordinate plane. The exploration builds on students' previous experiences with reflections. (See the Level 1 module, "Reflect on This.")

Materials List

- • graph paper (one sheet per student)
- • ruler (one per student)
- • MIRA™ (optional)

Technology

- • matrix manipulator
- • spreadsheet
- • geometry utility (optional)

Exploration

(page 234)

a.   **1–2.** Sample graph:

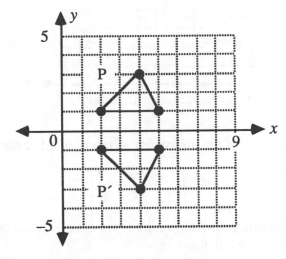

   3. Sample matrix:

$$\mathbf{P'} = \begin{bmatrix} 2 & 4 & 5 \\ -1 & -3 & -1 \end{bmatrix}$$

   4–5. The x-axis is the perpendicular bisector of the segments that connect the corresponding points of the preimage and image.

b.   **1–2.** Sample graph:

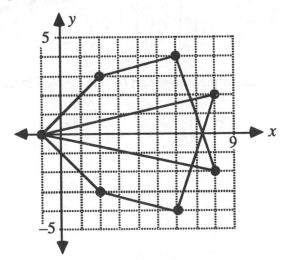

   3. Sample matrix:

$$\mathbf{H'} = \begin{bmatrix} -1 & 2 & 6 & 8 \\ 0 & -3 & -4 & 2 \end{bmatrix}$$

287

c. The following sample graph shows the triangle represented by matrix **P** reflected in the y-axis:

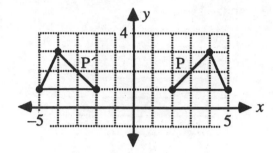

The coordinates of the image can be represented in the matrix below:

$$\mathbf{P'} = \begin{bmatrix} -2 & -4 & -5 \\ 1 & 3 & 1 \end{bmatrix}$$

The following sample graph shows the quadrilateral represented by matrix **H** reflected in the y-axis:

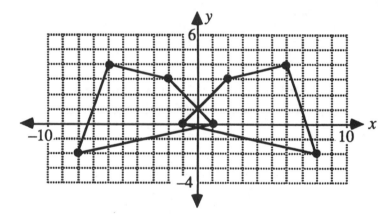

The coordinates of the image can be represented in the matrix below:

$$\mathbf{H'} = \begin{bmatrix} 1 & -2 & -6 & -8 \\ 0 & 3 & 4 & -2 \end{bmatrix}$$

d. **1.** Sample graph:

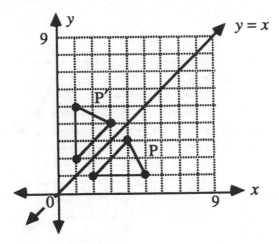

2. Sample image matrix:

$$\mathbf{P}' = \begin{bmatrix} 1 & 3 & 1 \\ 2 & 4 & 5 \end{bmatrix}$$

3. Sample graph:

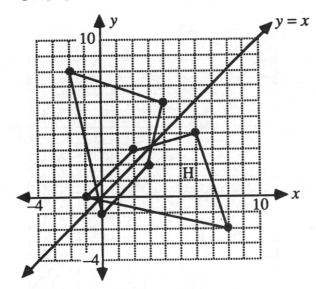

The coordinates of the image can be represented in the matrix below:

$$\mathbf{H}' = \begin{bmatrix} 0 & 3 & 4 & -2 \\ -1 & 2 & 6 & 8 \end{bmatrix}$$

289

e. Sample graph for the triangle represented by matrix **P**:

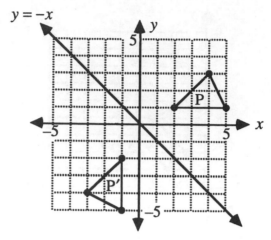

The coordinates of the image can be represented in the matrix below:

$$P' = \begin{bmatrix} -1 & -3 & -1 \\ -2 & -4 & -5 \end{bmatrix}$$

Sample graph for the quadrilateral represented by matrix **H**:

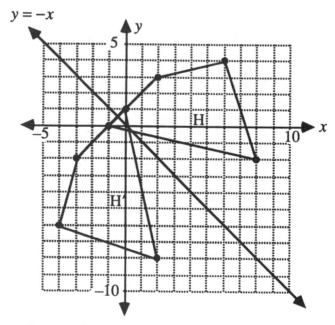

The coordinates of the image can be represented in the matrix below:

$$H' = \begin{bmatrix} 0 & -3 & -4 & 2 \\ -1 & -2 & -6 & -8 \end{bmatrix}$$

f. Matrix **A** reflects a set of points with respect to the line $y = x$. Matrix **B** reflects a set of points with respect to the y-axis. Matrix **C** reflects a set of points with respect to the line $y = -x$. Matrix **D** reflects a set of points with respect to the x-axis.

Discussion (page 236)

a. **1.** Sample response: When reflecting in the x-axis, the x-values remain unchanged but each y-value is the additive inverse of the corresponding y-value in the preimage.

   2. Sample response: When reflecting in the y-axis, the y-values remain unchanged but each x-value is the additive inverse of the corresponding x-value in the preimage.

b. **1.** Sample response: When reflecting in the line $y = x$, the x and y-values are switched.

   2. Sample response: When reflecting in the line $y = -x$, the x and y-values are switched and the signs are changed.

c. Sample responses: Both rotations and reflections use multiplication on the left by 2×2 matrices. Dilations use scalar multiplication or matrix multiplication. Translations use matrix addition. The number of columns in a translation matrix depends on the number of points being transformed.

d. Sample response: Dilations produce images that are similar to the preimage. Translations, rotations, and reflections produce images that are congruent to the preimage.

Assignment (page 236)

5.1 **a.** Sample response:

$$\mathbf{F'} = \mathbf{B} \cdot \mathbf{F}$$

$$= \begin{bmatrix} -1 & 0 \\ 0 & 1 \end{bmatrix} \cdot \begin{bmatrix} 2 & 3.5 & 6.5 & 7.5 & 6 & 3 \\ 4 & 6 & 6 & 4 & 3 & 3 \end{bmatrix}$$

   b. $\mathbf{F'} = \begin{bmatrix} -2 & -3.5 & -6.5 & -7.5 & -6 & -3 \\ 4 & 6 & 6 & 4 & 3 & 3 \end{bmatrix}$

   c. Sample graph:

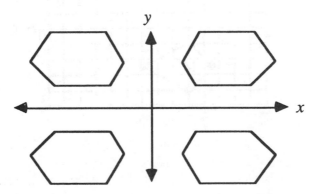

291

d. Sample response: No, you can't. For any preimage, one of the three possible images is the result of two reflections: one in the *x*-axis and one in the *y*-axis. Therefore, there is always one image that cannot be created by a single reflection.

*5.2 Answers will vary. The following sample graph shows Skip reflected in the line $y = -x$, then in the *y*-axis.

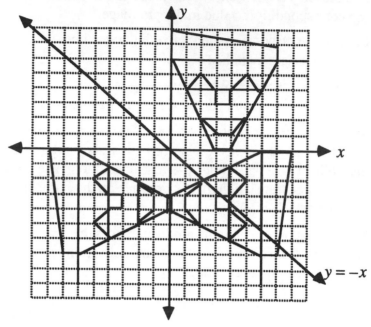

5.3 a–b. The coordinates of the vertices are (–0.5,–2.5), (1,–4), (4,–2.5), and (1,–1). Sample graph:

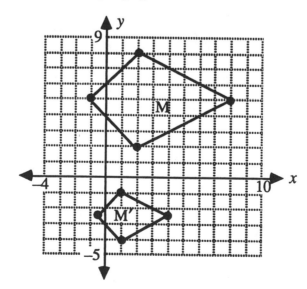

c. The composite transformation can be described by the matrix equation below:

$$M'' = 0.5 \cdot D \cdot M$$

$$= 0.5 \cdot \begin{bmatrix} 1 & 0 \\ 0 & -1 \end{bmatrix} \cdot \begin{bmatrix} -1 & 2 & 8 & 2 \\ 5 & 8 & 5 & 2 \end{bmatrix}$$

$$= \begin{bmatrix} -0.5 & 1 & 4 & -0.5 \\ -2.5 & -4 & -2.5 & -2.5 \end{bmatrix}$$

5.4 a–c. Students should observe that a reflection in the *x*-axis, followed by a reflection in the*y*-axis, is equivalent to a 180° rotation about the origin. Multiplication of the corresponding matrices confirms this result.

*5.5 a. A regular hexagon has six lines of symmetry, as shown below.

b. A line has an infinite number of lines of symmetry, including line *l* itself and all lines perpendicular to line *l*.

c. An ellipse has two lines of symmetry, as shown below.

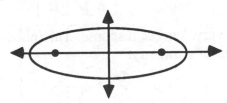

d. A circle has an infinite number of lines of symmetry, which all intersect at the center *C*.

5.6 Sample response: Skip does not have a line of symmetry, unless we exclude his hat.

* * * * *

5.7 a. Matrix **Z** is a reflection of **D** in the line $y = -x$.

b. The matrix that describes this transformation is:

$$R = \begin{bmatrix} 0 & -1 \\ -1 & 0 \end{bmatrix}$$

293

c. The following matrix equation verifies the responses given above:

$$\mathbf{R \cdot D = Z}$$

$$\begin{bmatrix} 0 & -1 \\ -1 & 0 \end{bmatrix} \bullet \begin{bmatrix} -3 & -6 & -4 & -2 \\ 1 & 2 & 4 & 3 \end{bmatrix} = \begin{bmatrix} -1 & -2 & -4 & -3 \\ 3 & 6 & 4 & 2 \end{bmatrix}$$

5.8   **a.** These do not create equivalent transformations. An example for $P(3,4)$ is shown below.

$$4 \bullet \begin{bmatrix} 3 \\ 4 \end{bmatrix} + \begin{bmatrix} -2 \\ 5 \end{bmatrix} \neq 4 \bullet \left(\begin{bmatrix} 3 \\ 4 \end{bmatrix} + \begin{bmatrix} -2 \\ 5 \end{bmatrix} \right)$$

$$\begin{bmatrix} 10 \\ 21 \end{bmatrix} \neq \begin{bmatrix} 4 \\ 36 \end{bmatrix}$$

b. These create equivalent transformations, as shown below for $P(a,b)$.

$$7 \bullet \left(\begin{bmatrix} 0 & 1 \\ 1 & 0 \end{bmatrix} \bullet \begin{bmatrix} a \\ b \end{bmatrix} \right) = \left(7 \bullet \begin{bmatrix} a \\ b \end{bmatrix} \right) \bullet \begin{bmatrix} 0 & 1 \\ 1 & 0 \end{bmatrix}$$

$$\begin{bmatrix} 7b \\ 7a \end{bmatrix} = \begin{bmatrix} 7b \\ 7a \end{bmatrix}$$

c. These create equivalent transformations, as shown below for $P(a,b)$.

$$\begin{bmatrix} 0 & -1 \\ -1 & 0 \end{bmatrix} \bullet \left(\begin{bmatrix} -1 & 0 \\ 0 & 1 \end{bmatrix} \bullet \begin{bmatrix} a \\ b \end{bmatrix} \right) = \begin{bmatrix} 0 & -1 \\ 1 & 0 \end{bmatrix} \bullet \begin{bmatrix} a \\ b \end{bmatrix}$$

$$\begin{bmatrix} -b \\ a \end{bmatrix} = \begin{bmatrix} -b \\ a \end{bmatrix}$$

5.9   Answers will vary. Sample response: The following regular heptagon has seven lines of symmetry.

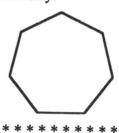

* * * * * * * * * *

Research Project   (page 239)

The flip-card cartoons should demonstrate students' knowledge of the various transformations and their matrix representations.

Answers to Summary Assessment (page 240)

1. **Note:** This problem was designed to be completed on a calculator capable of storing three matrices. It is adaptable to other types of technology and may be done in stages on a spreadsheet.

   a. The graph of the triangle should include the vertices (0,0), (16,0), and (16,16).

   b. 1. Sample translation matrix:

   $$T = \begin{bmatrix} -2 & -2 & -2 \\ 6 & 6 & 6 \end{bmatrix}$$

   2. The rotation matrix is shown below.

   $$R = \begin{bmatrix} 0 & -1 \\ 1 & 0 \end{bmatrix}$$

   3. This dilation may be accomplished through scalar multiplication or through multiplication on the left by the following matrix:

   $$D = \begin{bmatrix} 3/4 & 0 \\ 0 & 3/4 \end{bmatrix}$$

   c. Repeating the composite transformation produces a succession of triangles defined by the following matrices:

   $$A' = \begin{bmatrix} -9/2 & -9/2 & -33/2 \\ -3/2 & 21/2 & 21/2 \end{bmatrix}$$

   $$A'' = \begin{bmatrix} -27/8 & -99/8 & -99/8 \\ -39/8 & -39/8 & -111/8 \end{bmatrix}$$

   $$A''' = \begin{bmatrix} -27/32 & -27/32 & 182/32 \\ -129/32 & -345/32 & -345/32 \end{bmatrix}$$

   $$A'''' = \begin{bmatrix} -189/128 & 459/128 & 459/128 \\ -273/128 & -273/128 & 395/128 \end{bmatrix}$$

Sample graph:

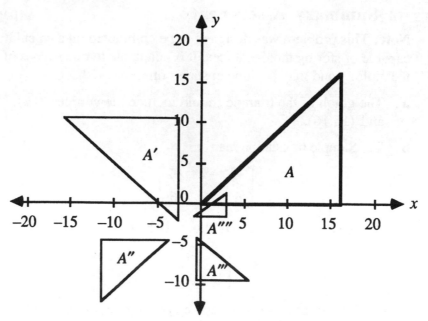

2. Responses will vary. Students should describe their results mathematically.

1.   **a.** Write a matrix equation that describes a dilation, with center at the origin and a scale factor of $3/4$, of the polygon defined by matrix **M** below.

$$\mathbf{M} = \begin{bmatrix} 2 & 1 & -4 & -8 & -3 \\ -1 & 4 & 5 & 1 & -3 \end{bmatrix}$$

      b. Determine the scale factor of the dilation, with center at the origin that, transforms **M** into **M′**.

$$\mathbf{M'} = \begin{bmatrix} 0.5 & 0.25 & -1 & -2 & -0.75 \\ -0.25 & 1 & 1.25 & 0.25 & -0.75 \end{bmatrix}$$

2.   **a.** Graph the triangles described by matrices **H** and **H′**.

$$\mathbf{H} = \begin{bmatrix} 7 & -6 & 2 \\ 2 & -1 & 8 \end{bmatrix} \qquad \mathbf{H'} = \begin{bmatrix} 17 & 4 & 12 \\ 1 & -2 & 7 \end{bmatrix}$$

      b. Identify the transformation of the preimage that occurred in Part **a**.

      c. Use a matrix equation to verify your response to Part **b**.

3.   **a.** Graph the triangle described by matrix **N** below and rotate it 180° about the origin.

$$\mathbf{N} = \begin{bmatrix} -5 & 5 & 1 \\ 4 & 4 & 0 \end{bmatrix}$$

      b. Write a matrix equation that describes this rotation.

4.   **a.** Graph the line segments described by matrices **S** and **S′**.

$$\mathbf{S} = \begin{bmatrix} -3 & 2 \\ 7 & 1 \end{bmatrix} \qquad \mathbf{S'} = \begin{bmatrix} -10 & 0 \\ 6 & -6 \end{bmatrix}$$

      b. Describe a composite transformation that could have generated **S′** from **S**. Use a matrix equation to support your response.

5.   **a.** Graph a quadrilateral on a coordinate plane.

    b. Transform the quadrilateral using three of the four transformations listed below. Graph each image in your composite transformation and write the matrix equation that describes each one.

- a dilation with center at the origin and a scale factor of 2/3

- a translation 8 units to the left and 3 units up

- a 270° rotation about the origin

- a reflection in the line $y = -x$

    c. Perform the three transformations you selected in Part **b** in a different order. Graph each image in the composite transformation and write the matrix equation that describes each one.

    d. Write a paragraph comparing the final image in Part **b** with the final image in Part **c**.

Answers to Module Assessment

1.   **a.** Sample matrix equation:

$$0.75 \cdot \begin{bmatrix} 2 & 1 & -4 & -8 & -3 \\ -1 & 4 & 5 & 1 & -3 \end{bmatrix} = \begin{bmatrix} 1.5 & 0.75 & -3 & -6 & -2.25 \\ -0.75 & 3 & 3.75 & 0.75 & -2.25 \end{bmatrix}$$

       b. The scale factor that dilates matrix **M** to matrix **M′** is 1/4.

2.   **a.** Sample graph:

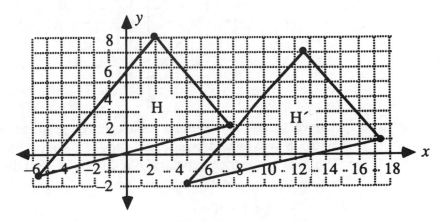

       b. The transformation is a translation 10 units to the right and 1 unit down.

       c. Sample matrix equation:

$$\begin{bmatrix} 7 & -6 & 2 \\ 2 & -1 & 8 \end{bmatrix} + \begin{bmatrix} 10 & 10 & 10 \\ -1 & -1 & -1 \end{bmatrix} = \begin{bmatrix} 17 & 4 & 12 \\ 1 & -2 & 7 \end{bmatrix}$$

3.   **a.** Sample graph:

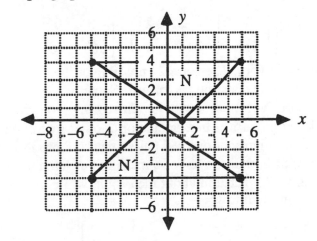

       b. Sample matrix equation:

$$\begin{bmatrix} -1 & 0 \\ 0 & -1 \end{bmatrix} \cdot \begin{bmatrix} -5 & 5 & 1 \\ 4 & 4 & 0 \end{bmatrix} = \begin{bmatrix} 5 & -5 & -1 \\ -4 & -4 & 0 \end{bmatrix}$$

4.   **a.** Sample graph:

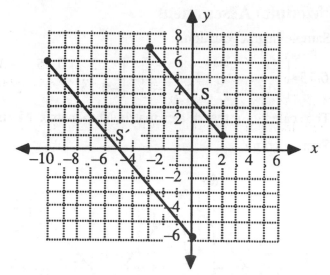

b. Answers may vary. Sample response: The segment represented by matrix **S** was dilated by a scale factor of 2 with center at the origin. The image was then translated 4 units left and 8 units down. A matrix equation describing this composite transformation is:

$$2S + T = S'$$

$$2\begin{bmatrix} -3 & 2 \\ 7 & 1 \end{bmatrix} + \begin{bmatrix} -4 & -4 \\ -8 & -8 \end{bmatrix} = \begin{bmatrix} -10 & 0 \\ 6 & -6 \end{bmatrix}$$

It is also possible that the segment represented by matrix **S** was translated 2 units left and 4 units down. This image was then dilated by a scale factor of 2 with center at the origin. In this case, the corresponding matrix equation is:

$$2(S + T) = S'$$

$$2\left(\begin{bmatrix} -3 & 2 \\ 7 & 1 \end{bmatrix} + \begin{bmatrix} -2 & -2 \\ -4 & -4 \end{bmatrix}\right) = \begin{bmatrix} -10 & 0 \\ 6 & -6 \end{bmatrix}$$

5.   Answers will vary. There are 24 possible orders in which the specified transformations could be performed. Some of the orders produce the same result. **Note:** For assistance in scoring, you may wish to store the following matrices in a calculator or other matrix manipulator. When added to the matrix of ordered pairs, matrix **T** produces a translation. When multiplied on the left of a matrix of ordered pairs, matrix **R** produces a 270° rotation about the origin, while matrix **X** produces a reflection in the line $y = -x$.

$$T = \begin{bmatrix} -8 & -8 & -8 & -8 \\ 3 & 3 & 3 & 3 \end{bmatrix} \qquad R = \begin{bmatrix} 0 & 1 \\ -1 & 0 \end{bmatrix} \qquad X = \begin{bmatrix} 0 & -1 \\ -1 & 0 \end{bmatrix}$$

Selected References

Barasch, M. *Theories of Art: From Plato to Winkelman*. New York: New York University Press, 1985.

Hulse, C. *The Rule of Art: Literature and Painting in the Renaissance*. Chicago: University of Chicago Press, 1990.

Papy, G. *Modern Mathematics*. London: Collier-Macmillan, 1968.

Flashbacks

Activity 1

1.1   **a.** Use the Pythagorean theorem to find the length of the hypotenuse of each right triangle in the following diagram.

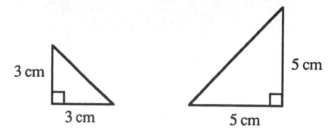

   b. Are these two triangles similar? Explain your response.

1.2.   Consider the following points: $A(1,2)$, $B(-3,4)$, $C(0,5)$, and $D(2,0)$.

   a. **1.** Find the equation of the line that contains A and B.

   2. Find the equation of the line that contains C and D.

   b. Identify the point of intersection of the two lines in Part **a**.

Activity 2

2.1.   Complete the following operations given matrices **A** and **B** below.

$$A = \begin{bmatrix} 2 & 6 & 8 \\ -9 & 6 & -2 \\ 6 & -1 & 9 \end{bmatrix} \quad B = \begin{bmatrix} 4 & 0 & -1 \\ 0 & 1 & 3 \\ 2 & -1 & 4 \end{bmatrix}$$

   a. $A + B$

   b. $3A$

   c. $A \bullet B$

2.2   Is it possible to perform the matrix multiplication shown below? Explain your response:

$$\begin{bmatrix} 2 & 3 & 4 \\ 9 & 2 & 1 \end{bmatrix} \bullet \begin{bmatrix} 3 & 4 & -9 \\ 4 & 5 & 0 \end{bmatrix}$$

Activity 3

3.1   Find the lengths of $\overline{AB}$ and $\overline{CD}$ in the diagram below.

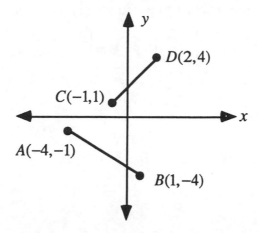

3.2   What angle measure corresponds with a tangent of 0.25?

3.3   Determine the measure of $\angle A$ in the following right triangle.

Activity 4

4.1   Graph the figure described by each of the following matrices on a coordinate plane.

a. $\begin{bmatrix} -2 & 5 \\ 1 & -6 \end{bmatrix}$

b. $\begin{bmatrix} 2 & 5 & 6 & 1 \\ 4 & -1 & -5 & -3 \end{bmatrix}$

4.2   Determine the unknown lengths in the triangle below.

Activity 5

5.1   Describe the graphs of $y = x$ and $y = -x$.

5.2   Complete the following operations given matrices **A**, **B**, and **C** below.

$$A = \begin{bmatrix} 2 & 4 & 7 & 4 & -6 \\ 7 & -1 & 0 & 0 & -4 \end{bmatrix} \qquad B = \begin{bmatrix} 2 & 2 & 2 & 2 \\ 7 & 7 & 7 & 7 \end{bmatrix} \qquad C = \begin{bmatrix} 0 & 1 \\ 1 & 0 \end{bmatrix}$$

a. $C \cdot A$

b. $C \cdot (A + B)$

Answers to Flashbacks

Activity 1

1.1   **a.** $\sqrt{3^2 + 3^2} = \sqrt{18} \approx 4.24$ cm; $\sqrt{5^2 + 5^2} = \sqrt{50} \approx 7.07$

      b. Sample response: Yes, the two triangles are similar. The corresponding angles are congruent and the corresponding sides are proportional. The ratio of corresponding sides is 3/5.

1.2   **a.** **1.** Sample response:

$$y - 4 = \frac{4-2}{-3-1}(x-(-3))$$
$$y = -0.5x + 2.5$$

        2. Sample response:

$$y - 0 = \frac{5-0}{0-2}(x-2)$$
$$y = -2.5x + 5$$

      b. $(1.25, 1.875)$

Activity 2

2.1   **a.** $A + B = \begin{bmatrix} 6 & 6 & 7 \\ -9 & 7 & 1 \\ 8 & -2 & 13 \end{bmatrix}$

      b. $3A = \begin{bmatrix} 6 & 18 & 24 \\ -27 & 18 & -6 \\ 18 & -3 & 27 \end{bmatrix}$

      c. $A \cdot B = \begin{bmatrix} 24 & -2 & 48 \\ -40 & 8 & 19 \\ 42 & -10 & 27 \end{bmatrix}$

2.2   Sample response: It is not possible to multiply a 2×3 matrix by another 2×3 matrix. The number of columns in the left-hand matrix must equal the number of rows in the right-hand matrix.

Activity 3

3.1 $AB = \sqrt{3^2 + 5^2} = \sqrt{34} \approx 5.83$; $CD = \sqrt{3^2 + 3^2} = \sqrt{18} \approx 4.24$

3.2 $\tan^{-1}(0.25) \approx 14°$

3.3 $m\angle A \approx 53°$

Activity 4

4.1   **a.** Sample graph:

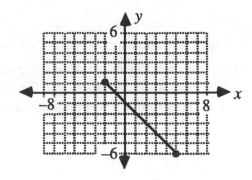

b. Sample graph:

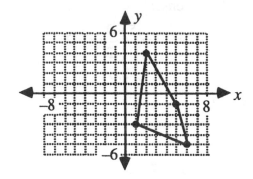

4.2 $y = \sqrt{3}/2 \approx 0.87;\ x = 1/2$

Activity 5

5.1   Sample response: Both graphs are lines that pass through the origin. The slope of $y = x$ is 1; the slope of $y = -x$ is -1.

5.2   **a.** $\begin{bmatrix} 7 & -1 & 0 & 0 & -4 \\ 2 & 4 & 7 & 4 & -6 \end{bmatrix}$

b. $\begin{bmatrix} 0 & 6 & 7 & 7 & 3 \\ 4 & 6 & 9 & 6 & -4 \end{bmatrix}$

Template for Problem 2.7

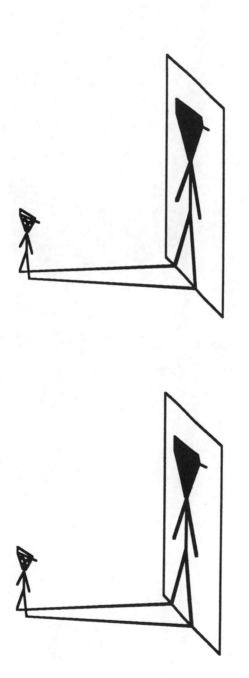

Hurry! Hurry! Hurry!
Step Right Up!

Have you ever played a carnival game? Better yet, have you ever won a big prize? In this module, you use probability to explore the carnival midway.

Bill Chalgren • Mike Trudnowski • Anne Watkins

Hurry! Hurry! Hurry! Step Right Up!

Overview

This module uses gaming situations to introduce geometric probability and conditional probability. Students also determine multistage probabilities involving independent events and use expected value to evaluate fair games.

Objectives

In this module, students will:

- use geometric models for determining probability
- use expected value to determine fair games
- explore probabilities of multistage experiments
- examine the difference between independent and dependent events
- explore conditional probability.

Prerequisites

For this module, students should know:

- how to determine the area of regular polygons and circles
- how to graph inequalities on a coordinate plane
- how to create tree diagrams and use them to determine probabilities
- how to identify the sample space for an experiment
- how to determine theoretical and experimental probabilities
- how to calculate expected value.

Time Line

Activity	1	2	3	Summary Assessment	Total
Days	3	2	4	1	10

Materials Required

Materials	Activity			
	1	**2**	**3**	**Summary Assessment**
dimes	X			
quarters	X			
centimeter graph paper	X			
cardboard	X			
tape	X			
rulers	X			
dice		X		
ping-pong balls			X	
markers			X	
paper bags			X	

Technology

Software	Activity			
	1	**2**	**3**	**Summary Assessment**
random number generator			X	

Hurry! Hurry! Hurry! Step Right Up!

Introduction (page 247)

This module uses carnival games to introduce geometric models for determining probability.

Discussion (page 247)

a. Sample response: The spinner has a better chance because it appears to win half the time. The dart looks like it has less than a 50% chance of winning.

b. Sample response: It is necessary to use the tip so that a single point determines the part of the board in which the spinner lands. If the entire head of the arrow is considered, the spinner could land in more than one part of the board.

c. **1.** Students may mention tossing rings onto the necks of pop bottles, throwing a ball through an opening, shooting at a target with an air rifle, using a sledgehammer to ring a bell, shooting a basketball through a hoop, throwing darts at balloons, knocking over bottles with a ball, playing a raffle, or catching metal disks with a magnet attached to a fishing pole.

   2. Some games, such as shooting baskets or throwing darts, involve at least some degree of skill. Others, such as raffles or bingo, are based on chance. Still others involve a mix of chance and skill.

d. Answers will vary. Students may prefer the dart game because at least some skill is involved. Others may choose the spinner game, arguing that the chances of winning seem better. **Note:** Students are not expected to calculate the probabilities of winning at this time. This situation is revisited in Problem **1.5**.

e. Since most carnival games are designed for both entertainment and profit-making, they are usually not fair games in the mathematical sense. Many carnival games allow few winners, or offer inexpensive prizes, to keep the expected value low. Some students may argue that foul play also makes some games unfair (for example, bottles that can't be knocked over or bent rifle barrels).

313

Activity 1

In this activity, students use geometric models to determine probability.

Materials List

- dimes (one per group)
- quarters (one per group)
- centimeter graph paper (one sheet per group)
- rulers (one per group)
- cardboard (four sheets per group)
- tape

Teacher Note

This exploration works well for groups of two students. After one student drops the coin onto the grid, the other can judge and record wins or losses.

Exploration

(page 248)

Students play the coin-drop game and record the experimental outcomes.

a.   Students create a game board with four walls around it.

b–c.   **Note:** If dimes are dropped from too great a height, they may bounce over the walls. Placing a notebook under the grid can reduce bouncing.

d.   Experimental probabilities will vary. The theoretical probability of winning is approximately 0.16.

e.   1. Answers may vary. Given a dime with a radius of 0.9 cm, the center of the dime must be at least 0.9 cm from each line on the grid.

2. Using the center of the dime as a reference point, the region that models all winning outcomes is a square within the 3 cm × 3 cm square. The following diagram shows eight possible positions for winning dimes, the centers of these dimes, and the square formed by the centers of all winning coins.

314

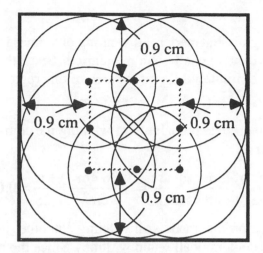

The area of the region that models winning outcomes is approximately $(3-(2 \bullet 0.9))^2 = 1.44$ cm^2.

3. The theoretical probability can be determined by dividing the area of the inner square (representing all winning outcomes) by the area of the outer square (representing all possible outcomes):

$$\frac{\text{area of inner square}}{\text{area of outer square}} = \frac{1.44 \text{ cm}^2}{9 \text{ cm}^2} = \frac{4}{25} = 0.16$$

f. Answers will vary. For a large number of trials, the experimental probability is likely to approximate the theoretical probability.

Discussion

(page 250)

a. Sample response: If any other point is used, the orientation of the coin would have to be considered when determining the area that represents a win. This would make the problem very hard to solve.

b. Assuming that the walls are at least 0.9 cm from the grid, the probability of winning is the same for any number of squares (n):

$$\frac{n \bullet \text{area of inner square}}{n \bullet \text{area of outer square}} = \frac{1.44n}{9n} = \frac{1.44}{9} = \frac{4}{25} = 0.16$$

c. Answers will vary. These probabilities may or may not be approximately equal, depending on the class results. For a large number of trials, the experimental probability is likely to be close to the theoretical probability.

d. Sample response: The game could be made impossible to play by using a coin with a diameter that is greater than the dimensions of the squares, or by using squares with dimensions that are less than the diameter of the dime.

Assignment (page 251)

1.1   **a.** The region that models all winning outcomes is the square formed by the centers of all winning quarters. Since the radius of a quarter is approximately 1.2 cm, the area of this region can be found as follows: $(3 - (2 \bullet 1.2))^2 = 0.36 \text{ cm}^2$.

        b. The theoretical probability of winning the coin-drop game using a quarter is:

$$\frac{\text{area of inner square}}{\text{area of outer square}} = \frac{0.36 \text{ cm}^2}{9 \text{ cm}^2} = \frac{1}{25} = 0.04$$

*1.2   **a.** The region that models all winning outcomes is the square formed by the centers of all winning dimes. Since the radius of a dime is approximately 0.9 cm, the area of this region can be found as follows: $(4 - (2 \bullet 0.9))^2 = 4.84 \text{ cm}^2$.

        b. The theoretical probability of winning this version of the game is:

$$\frac{\text{area of inner square}}{\text{area of outer square}} = \frac{4.84 \text{ cm}^2}{16 \text{ cm}^2} = \frac{121}{400} = 0.3025$$

1.3   **a.** Using a geometric model, the probability of landing in the yellow ring is the ratio of the area of the yellow ring to the area of the entire target:

$$\frac{\pi(10)^2 - \pi(7)^2}{\pi(13)^2} = \frac{\pi(51)}{\pi(169)} = \frac{51}{169} \approx 0.30$$

        b. Sample response: No. It is not really a random event because players can aim the dart at a particular point.

*1.4   **a.** As shown in the diagram below, students can consider all the positions of the ball's center that will knock down the pin:

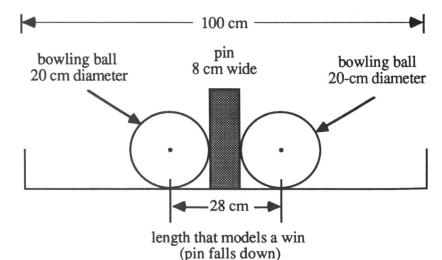

length that models a win
(pin falls down)

316

Using this geometric model, the width of all possible paths of the ball's center down the lane is $(100 - 2 \bullet 10)$, or 80 cm. The width of the paths that result in knocking down the pin is 28 cm. The probability of winning is $28/80 = 7/20 = 0.35$.

b. As shown in the diagram below, if the pin is placed against one rail, the ball can pass on only one side of the pin. Since the center of the ball can pass no closer than 10 cm from the rail, the width of the paths that result in knocking down the pin is 8 cm. This reduces the probability of winning to $8/80 = 1/10 = 0.1$.

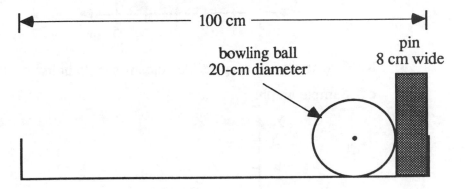

1.5 Sample response: I would rather play the spinner game because the probability of winning is greater. Since each of the four central angles where the spinner is located measure 90°, the probability that the spinner lands in the unshaded portion of the board is:

$$\frac{90° + 90°}{360°} = 0.5$$

The probability of a dart landing in the unshaded portion of the board is the sum of areas of the two unshaded rectangles, divided by the total area of the board:

$$\frac{40 \bullet 70 + 40 \bullet 90}{130 \bullet 110} \approx 0.448$$

* * * * *

317

*1.6   **a .** Sample graph:

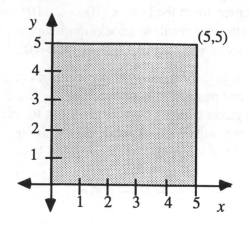

b . The area of all the possible outcomes is 25 units^2.

c . Sample graph:

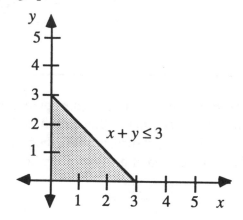

The area of the shaded region is $1/2\,(3)(3) = 4.5$ units^2.

d . Using a geometric model, the probability that $x + y \le 3$ is $4.5/25 = 0.18$.

e. The following sample graph shows the region bounded by $x + y \geq 6$, $0 \leq x \leq 5$, and $0 \leq y \leq 5$.

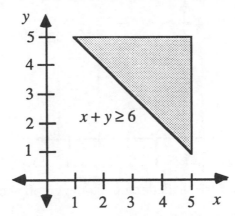

The area of the shaded region is $1/2(4)(4) = 8$ units^2. Using a geometric model, the probability that $x + y \geq 6$ is $8/25 = 0.32$.

*1.7   **a.** Sample sketch:

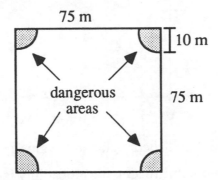

b. Sample response: The dangerous area is a circle with a radius of 10 m. Therefore, the area of the parking lot in which it is safe to land is: $75^2 - \pi 10^2 \approx 5300$ m^2.

c. **1.** Using a geometric model, the probability that the parachutist lands safely can be found as follows:

$$\frac{\text{safe area}}{\text{parking lot area}} \approx \frac{5300}{5625} \approx 0.94$$

2. The probability that the parachute's lines get tangled in a security light is:

$$\frac{\text{unsafe area}}{\text{parking lot area}} \approx \frac{\pi 10^2}{75^2} \approx \frac{314}{5625} \approx 0.06$$

d. Sample response: The probabilities in Part **c** add to 1 because they are complementary events.

1.8   **a.** Sample graph:

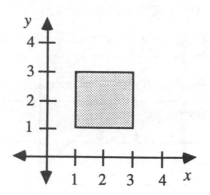

   b. The area of the shaded region in the graph above is 4 units^2.

   c. Sample graph:

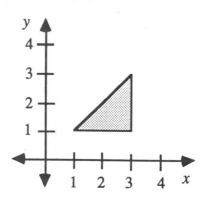

The area of the shaded region in the graph above is 2 units^2.

   d. Using a geometric model, the probability is $2/4 = 0.5$.

   e. Using a geometric model, the probability is $2/4 = 0.5$. **Note:** The events described in Parts **d** and **e** are not complementary, since the points on the line $y = x$ are included in both.

* * * * * * * * * *

(page 254)

Activity 2

In this activity, students calculate expected value and determine whether or not a game is mathematically fair.

Materials List

- dice (one per group)

Exploration

a–b. Students should recognize that the chances of winning each prize are not equally likely.

c. The theoretical probability of winning each prize is shown below.

Value of Prize	Roll of Die	Probability
$1.50	1	1/6
$1.00	2	1/6
$0.50	3	1/6
$0.00	4	1/6
$0.00	5	1/6
$0.00	6	1/6

Since three of the outcomes result in a prize of $0.00, its theoretical probability is $1/6 + 1/6 + 1/6 = 3/6 = 1/2$.

d. The experimental probabilities may or may not approximate the theoretical probabilities.

e. The expected value can be found as follows:

$$\frac{1}{6} \cdot \$1.50 + \frac{1}{6} \cdot \$1.00 + \frac{1}{6} \cdot \$0.50 + \frac{1}{2} \cdot 0 = \$0.50$$

Discussion

a. Sample response: No. You are not equally likely to win each prize. A non-winning roll of 4, 5, or 6 is three times more likely to occur than any single winning roll.

b. Since the cost to play ($1.00) and the expected value ($0.50) are not equal, the game is not mathematically fair. To make the game fair, students may suggest reducing the cost to play, increasing the value of the prizes, or changing the probabilities of winning the prizes.

c. Answers will vary. To pay wages, travel costs, and other expenses, carnival operators must make a profit from their games. It would be unreasonable to expect a mathematically fair game under these circumstances.

Assignment

*2.1 To make this a fair game, the cost to play must equal the expected value:

$$\frac{1}{2} \cdot \$0.00 + \frac{1}{3} \cdot \$0.50 + \frac{1}{6} \cdot \$2.00 = \$0.50$$

2.2 **a.** The expected value can be calculated as follows:

$$\frac{21}{25} \cdot \$0.00 + \frac{4}{25} \cdot \$5.00 = \$0.80$$

b. To make the game mathematically fair, the cost to play must be decreased to $0.80.

c. The value of the prize that makes the game mathematically fair can be calculated as follows:

$$\frac{21}{25} \cdot \$0.00 + \frac{4}{25} \cdot x = \$1.00$$

$$x = \$6.25$$

*2.3 **a.** The expected value can be calculated as follows:

$$\frac{24}{25} \cdot \$0.00 + \frac{1}{25} \cdot \$15.00 = \$0.60$$

b. To make the game mathematically fair, the cost to play must be decreased to $0.60.

c. The value of the prize that makes the game mathematically fair can be calculated as follows:

$$\frac{24}{25} \cdot \$0.00 + \frac{1}{25} \cdot x = \$1.00$$

$$x = \$25.00$$

2.4 To make this a fair game, the cost to play must equal the expected value:

$$\frac{1}{13} \cdot \$10 + \frac{3}{13} \cdot \$1 + \frac{9}{13} \cdot \$0 = \$1.00$$

* * * * *

2.5 **a.** In the following sample graph, the shaded region represents all the possible pairs of numbers in the interval [0, 5] for which the sum is less than or equal to 3.

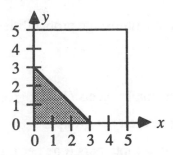

The probability of Juan winning is the area of the shaded region divided by the area of the square:

$$\frac{4.5}{25} = 0.18 = 18\%$$

b. Since Juan theoretically wins $0.50 in 18% of the games and loses $0.20 in 82% of the games, the expected value can be calculated as follows: $0.18 \bullet 0.50 + 0.82 \bullet -0.20 \approx -0.07$.

c. Sample response: Juan can expect to lose an average of approximately $0.07 each time he plays. Therefore, he should not play the game.

d. Answers will vary. Sample response: If Joan continues to pay Juan $0.50 each time he wins, then solving the following equation for x gives the amount Juan should pay Joan to make the expected value the same for both players.

$$0.18 \bullet \$0.50 = 0.82x$$

$$\$0.11 \approx x$$

If Juan continues to pay Joan $0.20 each time she wins, then solving the following equation for x gives the amount Joan should pay Juan to make the expected value the same for both players.

$$0.18x = 0.82 \bullet \$0.20$$

$$x \approx \$0.91$$

* * * * * * * * *

Research Project

(page 257)

After students have presented their games to the class, you may wish to ask them to discuss modifications that might make the games profitable at a carnival.

Activity 3

In this activity, students examine multistage probabilities.

Materials List

- ping-pong balls or other small objects (10 per group)
- red and blue markers (one each per group)
- paper bags or other opaque containers (one per group)

Technology

- random number generator

Exploration 1 (page 258)

Students simulate the fishing derby by drawing objects from a bag. **Note:** To ensure random draws, the objects should be indistinguishable by touch.

a–b. Students simulate the fishing derby 10 times, then combine their results with the class. Sample data for 100 trials:

Event	Points	Number of Occurrences	Experimental Probability
3 red	6	8	0.08
2 red, 1 blue	5	25	0.25
1 red, 2 blue	4	46	0.46
3 blue	3	21	0.21

c. Sample tree diagram:

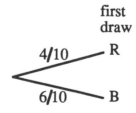

d. The eight possible outcomes are RRR, RRB, RBR, RBB, BRR, BRB, BBR, and BBB (where R represents red and B represents blue).
Sample tree diagram:

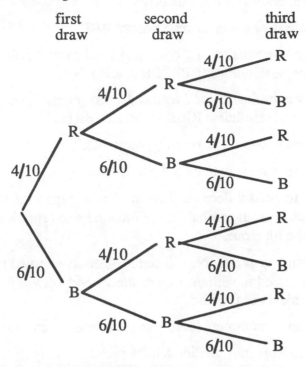

first draw   second draw   third draw

e. Students should calculate the following probabilities:

$P(\text{RRR}) = (4/10)^3 = 0.064$, $\ P(\text{RRB}) = (4/10)^2 \cdot 6/10 = 0.096$,

$P(\text{RBR}) = (4/10)^2 \cdot 6/10 = 0.096$, $\ P(\text{RBB}) = 4/10 \cdot (6/10)^2 = 0.144$,

$P(\text{BRR}) = 6/10 \cdot (4/10)^2 = 0.096$, $\ P(\text{BRB}) = (6/10)^2 \cdot 4/10 = 0.144$,

$P(\text{BBR}) = (6/10)^2 \cdot 4/10 = 0.144$, and $P(\text{BBB}) = (6/10)^3 = 0.216$.

f. **1.** The probabilities of winning each prize are as follows:
$P(6) = 0.064$, $\ P(5) = 3 \cdot 0.096 = 0.288$, $\ P(4) = 3 \cdot 0.144 = 0.432$,
and $P(3) = 0.216$.

2. For a large number of trials, the experimental probabilities are likely to be close to the theoretical probabilities.

Discussion 1 (page 259)

a. There are eight possible outcomes.

b. **1.** There is one way to get 3 points: BBB.

   2. Any combination of 2 blues and 1 red earns 4 points. There are three possibilities: BBR, BRB, and RBB.

   3. Any combination of 2 reds and 1 blue earns 5 points. There are three possibilities: RRB, RBR, and BRR.

   4. There is one way to earn 6 points: RRR.

   5. There is no way to earn 7 points.

c. Sample response: Because there are fewer rings with red dots than rings with blue dots, the probability of drawing a red ring is less than that of drawing a blue one.

d. **1.** Sample response: No. Since the object is returned to the container and mixed in with the others, the second draw is from the same set of objects as the first.

   2. Sample response: No, for the same reasons mentioned above.

e. Some students may predict that the rabbit's foot is the prize most often won because it requires the fewest points. Considering theoretical probabilities, however, the celebrity poster should be the most frequently awarded prize.

f. **1.** Answers may vary. Sample response: Generate random numbers from 1 to 10, inclusive. The numbers from 1 to 4 represent a red ring and earn 2 points. The numbers from 5 to 10 represent a blue ring and earn 1 point.

   2. Students may expect the simulations to produce the same results. Since each is repeated a relatively few number of times, however, the results are likely to vary. Over the long run, the simulations should produce similar results because they involve the same theoretical probabilities.

g. Sample response: Because it contains more trials, the class data should better represent the long-term results of the game. The experimental probability should be closer to the theoretical probability as the number of trials increases.

Exploration 2 (page 260)

In this exploration, students examine conditional probabilities by simulating a version of the fishing derby without replacement.

   a.   Responses will vary. Some students may observe that the probabilities of scoring 6 points (RRR) or 3 points (BBB) are decreased.

   b.   The possible outcomes are the same as those in the original version of the game: RRR, RRB, RBR, RBB, BRR, BRB, BBR, and BBB. Sample tree diagram:

   c.   Students should determine the probabilities of each outcome as follows:
$P(RRR) = 4/10 \cdot 3/9 \cdot 2/8 = 1/30 \approx 0.03$,
$P(RRB) = 4/10 \cdot 3/9 \cdot 6/8 = 1/10 = 0.1$,
$P(RBR) = 4/10 \cdot 6/9 \cdot 3/8 = 1/10 = 0.1$,
$P(RBB) = 4/10 \cdot 6/9 \cdot 5/8 = 1/6 \approx 0.17$,
$P(BRR) = 6/10 \cdot 4/9 \cdot 3/8 = 1/10 = 0.1$,
$P(BRB) = 6/10 \cdot 4/9 \cdot 5/8 = 1/6 \approx 0.17$,
$P(BBR) = 6/10 \cdot 5/9 \cdot 4/8 = 1/6 \approx 0.17$, and
$P(BBB) = 6/10 \cdot 5/9 \cdot 4/8 = 1/6 \approx 0.17$.

      Using these probabilities, the theoretical probabilities of obtaining each score are $P(6) = 1/30 \approx 0.03$, $P(5) = 3/10 = 0.3$, $P(4) = 3/6 = 0.5$, and $P(3) = 1/6 \approx 0.17$.

d. Students may design their own simulations using either a container of red and blue objects or a random number generator. Sample response: Generate random numbers from 1 to 10, inclusive. The numbers 1 to 4 represent the red rings and are worth 2 points. The numbers 5 to 10 represent the blue rings and are worth 1 point. During a single round of the simulation, any number that comes up more than once is ignored and another number generated.

e. The following table shows some sample data for 100 trials. In this case, the experimental probabilities closely approximate the theoretical probabilities.

Event	Points	Number of Occurrences	Experimental Probability
3 red	6	3	0.03
2 red, 1 blue	5	31	0.31
1 red, 2 blue	4	45	0.45
3 blue	3	21	0.21

Discussion 2

(page 261)

a. Sample response: When using a random number generator, ignoring any number that comes up more than once in a single round models its removal from the tank.

b. In the new version of the game, the theoretical probability of getting 6 points decreases from 0.064 to approximately 0.03.

c. Sample response: Although the chances of winning a hat have improved slightly, the chances of winning a bear have decreased. Overall, the chances of winning one or the other has also decreased. In the original game, the chances of winning a hat or a bear are $0.288 + 0.064 = 0.352$. In the new version, the chances of winning a hat or a bear are approximately $0.3 + 0.033 = 0.333$.

d. 1. Sample response: The probabilities are different because the first chip drawn is not replaced in the box. Since the numbers and kinds of chips in the box have changed, the probabilities must be adjusted.

   2. Since there is only one blue chip in the game, the probability of drawing two blue chips is 0.

Assignment

*3.1   **a.** Because all the outcomes result in a prize, and because the sum of their probabilities is 1, the probability of winning some prize in the fishing derby is 1.

   b. Because no combination of three rings adds up to 7 points, the probability of earning 7 points is 0.

   c. The expected value, in points, can be determined as follows:

$$\frac{8}{125} \bullet 6 + \frac{36}{125} \bullet 5 + \frac{54}{125} \bullet 4 + \frac{27}{125} \bullet 3 = 4.2$$

*3.2   **a.** The expected value, in points, is:

$$\frac{1}{30} \bullet 6 + \frac{3}{10} \bullet 5 + \frac{1}{2} \bullet 4 + \frac{1}{6} \bullet 3 = 4.2$$

   b. Answers will vary. The probabilities of winning a poster or hat increased slightly in the new version, while the probabilities of winning a key chain or teddy bear decreased.

3.3   **a.** Sample response: For the game to be fair, the expected value must equal the cost to play. The expected value of the original fishing derby is:

$$\frac{8}{125} \bullet \$2.00 + \frac{36}{125} \bullet \$0.80 + \frac{54}{125} \bullet \$0.60 + \frac{27}{125} \bullet \$0.25 \approx \$0.67$$

   One way to make this a fair game would be to reduce the cost to play to $0.67.

   b. Sample response: For the game to be fair, the expected value must equal the cost to play. The expected value of the new version is:

$$\frac{1}{30} \bullet \$2.00 + \frac{3}{10} \bullet \$0.80 + \frac{1}{2} \bullet \$0.60 + \frac{1}{6} \bullet \$0.25 \approx \$0.65$$

   One way to make this a fair game would be to reduce the cost to play to $0.65.

*3.4   **a.** There are four equally likely outcomes when tossing two coins: HH, HT, TH, and TT. Therefore, the probabilities of each result can be determined as follows: $P(1 \text{ step}) = P(\text{HT}) + P(\text{TH}) = 1/2 = 0.5$, $P(0 \text{ steps}) = P(\text{TT}) = 1/4 = 0.25$, and $P(-1 \text{ step}) = P(\text{HH}) = 1/4 = 0.25$.

   b. The expected value, in number of stairs, is:

$$\frac{1}{4} \bullet 0 + \frac{1}{2} \bullet 1 + \frac{1}{4} \bullet -1 = \frac{1}{4} = 0.25$$

c. Sample response: Since $10 \cdot 0.25 = 2.5$, Guinn is likely to be 2 or 3 steps up from the starting point.

d. If the game starts on the middle of the 25 stairs (or the 13th stair), a player must move up 12 stairs to win. On average, Guinn would need 48 turns ($12/0.25 = 48$) to get to the top step.

★ ★ ★ ★ ★

*3.5   **a.** The following tree diagram shows the probability of each outcome:

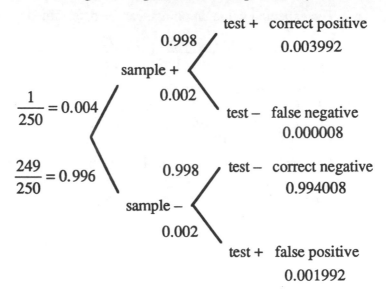

b. **1.** 3992

    2. 8

    3. 994,008

    4. 1992

c. Sample response: Of the 1,000,000 people tested, I expect $3992 + 1992 = 5984$ to test positive. Of these, only 3992 would actually have HIV, so $P(\text{HIV}|\text{Test} +) = 3992/5984 \approx 0.667$.

★ ★ ★ ★ ★ ★ ★ ★ ★

330

Answers to Summary Assessment (page 264)

1. Student responses should take the form of a letter and include the following information.

    a. The total area of the board is $30,000$ cm^2. The area of the red zones is $3(30 \cdot 35) = 3150$ cm^2. Assuming that the dart is equally likely to land anywhere on the board, the probability of landing in a red zone is $3150/30,000 = 21/200 = 0.105$.

    The area of the blue zone is $\pi(4^2) \approx 50$ cm^2. The probability of landing in the blue zone is approximately $50/30,000 \approx 0.002$. The probability of not landing in either winning zone is $(30,000 - 3150 - 50.27)/30,000 \approx 0.893$. **Note:** This may also be calculated by $1 - P(\text{red zone}) - P(\text{blue zone})$.

    b. The expected value can be calculated as follows:

    $$(0.893 \cdot \$0) + (0.105 \cdot \$25) + (0.002 \cdot \$10,000) \approx \$22.63$$

    c. Assuming no other costs, the lowest price the charity could charge to play, and still hope to earn some profit, is $23.00.

    d. For the first 1000 players, the charity should plan to award about $1000 \cdot 0.105 = 105$ miniature replicas, and $1000 \cdot 0.002 = 2$ full-sized cars.

    e. Since each game is an independent event, the probability that two players in a row win full-sized cars is approximately $0.002^2 \approx 0.000004$, or about 4 in 1,000,000.

    Student recommendations will vary. At a cost to play of $23.00, the charity could expect to earn an average of approximately $0.37 per player. Based on this small per-player profit, some students may recommend against using this game as fund-raiser. They may also mention the possibility of having to award a full-sized car before earning enough money to pay for it, or suggest that the high cost of playing may discourage potential players.

2. Student responses should again take the form of a letter. To determine
probabilities, some may construct a tree diagram like the one shown below:

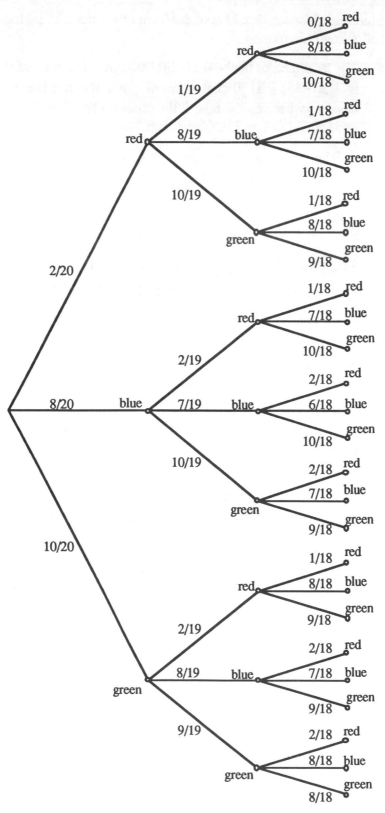

The probabilities and point values for each possible draw of three balls are shown in the following table.

Balls Drawn	Point Value	Probability
3 red	15	$0/6840 = 0.000$
2 red, 1 blue	12	$48/6840 \approx 0.007$
2 red, 1 green	11	$60/6840 \approx 0.009$
1 red, 2 blue	9	$336/6840 \approx 0.049$
1 red, 1 blue, 1 green	7	$960/6840 \approx 0.140$
1 red, 2 green	8	$540/6840 \approx 0.079$
3 blue	6	$336/6840 \approx 0.049$
2 blue, 1 green	5	$1680/6840 \approx 0.246$
1 blue, 2 green	4	$2160/6840 \approx 0.316$
3 green	3	$720/6840 \approx 0.105$

The probabilities for winning each prize can be calculated by adding the probabilities for the appropriate point values. The expected value for the game is shown in the table below.

Points	Prize Value	Probability	Product
[12, 15]	$3.00	$48/6840 \approx 0.007$	$0.02
[9, 11]	$1.75	$396/6840 \approx 0.058$	$0.10
[6, 8]	$0.40	$1836/6840 \approx 0.268$	$0.11
[3, 5]	$0.00	$4560/6840 \approx 0.667$	$0.00
		Expected Value	$0.23

Over the long term, the carnival can expect to earn an average profit of $0.77 per player. Based on this relatively large profit, students may recommend that the carnival add the game.

333

1. In one lottery game, each player purchases a ticket for $5.00, then selects a three-digit number. Each digit must be between 0 and 9, inclusive, and can appear only once in the number.

Lottery officials then randomly select three digits, one at a time and without replacement. These digits are recorded in the order selected to form a three-digit number.

If the player's three-digit number matches the number selected by the lottery, the player wins.

a. How many three-digit numbers are possible in this lottery game?

b. What is the probability of winning with one ticket?

c. If this were a fair game, how much should the lottery pay for matching the winning number? Justify your response.

2. A local convenience store is having a grand opening celebration. As part of its promotional activities, the store plans to offer prize tickets to everyone who enters the store. No purchase is necessary to win. The value of each prize and the probability of winning it are shown in the table below. What is the expected value for a prize ticket?

Prize	Value	Probability
soft drink	$1	0.05
two lottery tickets	$2	0.01
40 L of gasoline	$15	0.001
weekend vacation	$1000	0.000005
European vacation	$10,000	0.00000005

3. Consider a game in which three balls—numbered 1, 2, and 3—are placed in a paper bag. Player 1 draws a ball, records its number, then replaces it in the bag. Player 2 does the same. For each version of this game described below, determine whether you would want to be player 1 or player 2. Justify your responses.

a. If the sum x of the two numbers is odd, player 1 loses x points while player 2 wins x points. If the sum of the two numbers is even, player 2 loses 4 points, while player 1 wins 4 points.

b. If both players draw the same number, no points are won or lost. If the sum of the two numbers is even, the player with the higher number wins 5 points, while the other player loses 5 points. If the sum of the two numbers is odd, the player with the lower number wins 3 points, while the other player loses 3 points.

4. As described in Problem **3.4**, Guinn and Ebdul are playing the stair-step game. To reduce the time required to declare a winner, they decide to change the rules of the game.

 Ebdul suggests tossing four coins on each turn. If one head or three heads appear on a player's four coins, the player moves up one stair. If two or four heads appear, the player moves down one stair. If no heads appear, the player remains on the same step.

 As before, the game starts on the middle step of a staircase 25 steps long. To win the game, a player must reach the top step.

 a. If movement is described in terms of the number of stairs moved upwards, then each player's turn in the game has three possible results: 1 step, 0 steps, and –1 step.

   What is the probability of each of these results?

 b. What is the expected value, in number of stairs moved upwards, for each turn in this version of the game?

 c. Will Ebdul's suggestion shorten the stair-step game? Justify your response.

5. In the cube game, players toss a cube with three green faces, one red face, one white face, and one blue face into a bucket. After you toss the cube, the game operator tells you that the green face is not showing. Given this information, what is the probability that the red face is showing? Justify your response.

Answers to Module Assessment

1. **a.** There are $10 \bullet 9 \bullet 8 = 720$ possible numbers for this game.

  b. The probability that any one ticket wins is $1/720 \approx 0.001$.

  c. If this were a fair game, the expected value should equal the cost to play, or $5.00. Therefore, the prize should be worth $3600.

2. The expected value can be determined as follows:

$$(0.05 \bullet \$1) + (0.01 \bullet \$2) + (0.001 \bullet \$15) + (0.000005 \bullet \$1000) +$$
$$(0.00000005 \bullet \$10,000) + (0.93899495 \bullet \$0) \approx \$0.09$$

3. **a.** There are five possible sums: 2, 3, 4, 5, and 6. The probability of a 2 is 1/9, of a 3 is 2/9, of a 4 is $3/9 = 1/3$, of a 5 is 2/9, and of a 6 is 1/9. The expected value for player 1, in points, can be found as follows:

$$\frac{1}{9} \bullet 4 + \frac{2}{9} \bullet -3 + \frac{3}{9} \bullet 4 + \frac{2}{9} \bullet -5 + \frac{1}{9} \bullet 4 = \frac{4}{9}$$

The expected value for player 2 is:

$$\frac{1}{9} \bullet -4 + \frac{2}{9} \bullet 3 + \frac{3}{9} \bullet -4 + \frac{2}{9} \bullet 5 + \frac{1}{9} \bullet -4 = -\frac{4}{9}$$

In this case, player 1 has the advantage.

  b. The following table shows the number of points associated with each draw.

Number Drawn		Points Received	
Player 1	Player 2	Player 1	Player 2
1	1	0	0
1	2	3	−3
1	3	−5	5
2	1	−3	3
2	2	0	0
2	3	3	−3
3	1	5	−5
3	2	−3	3
3	3	0	0

Both players have three chances of winning 0 points; two chances of winning 3 points; two chances of winning −3 points; one chance of winning 5 points; and one chance of winning −5 points. The expected value for both players is:

$$\frac{3}{9} \bullet 0 + \frac{2}{9} \bullet 3 + \frac{2}{9} \bullet -3 + \frac{1}{9} \bullet 5 + \frac{1}{9} \bullet -5 = 0$$

In this case, neither player has an advantage.

4.   **a.** There are 16 equally likely outcomes when tossing four coins: HHHH, HHHT, HHTH, HHTT, HTHH, HTHT, HTTH, HTTT, THHH, THHT, THTH, THTT, TTHH, TTHT, TTTH, and TTTT. Therefore, the probabilities of each result can be determined as follows: $P(1 \text{ step}) = 1/2 = 0.5$, $P(0 \text{ steps}) = 1/16 = 0.0625$, and $P(-1 \text{ step}) = 7/16 = 0.4375$.

b. The expected value, in number of stairs, is:

$$\frac{1}{16} \bullet 0 + \frac{1}{2} \bullet 1 + \frac{7}{16} \bullet -1 = \frac{1}{16} = 0.0625$$

c. Sample response: The rule change would actually slow the game down. The expected movement per turn decreases from 0.25 steps to 0.0625 steps, a factor of 1/4. Therefore, one would expect the new version to take four times as long as the original game.

5.   Sample response: If the result of rolling the cube is not green, the roll must be either red, white, or blue. Each of these three colors appears once, so the probability of a red face is $1/3 \approx 0.33$.

Selected References

Dahlke, R., and R. Fakler. "Geometrical Probability—A Source of Interesting and Significant Applications of High School Mathematics." In *Readings for Enrichment in Secondary School Mathematics*, ed. by Max A. Sobel. Reston, VA: National Council of Teachers of Mathematics (NCTM), 1988.

Harshbarger, R. J., and J. J. Reynolds. *Finite Mathematics for Management, Life, and Social Sciences*. Lexington, MA: D.C. Heath and Co., 1992.

Heintz, R. E. "It's in the Bag." *Mathematics Teacher* 70 (February 1977): 132–36.

"The Laws of Probability." *Time* 85 (8 January 1965): 42.

North Carolina School of Science and Mathematics, Department of Mathematics and Computer Science. *Geometric Probability*. Reston, VA: NCTM, 1988.

"Trial by Mathematics." *Time* 91 (26 April 1968): 41.

Zuwaylif, F. H. *General Applied Sciences*. Reading, MA: Addison-Wesley, 1970.

Flashbacks

Activity 1

1.1 Find the area of the shaded region in Parts **a–d** below.

a.

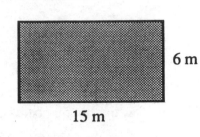

5 m

32°

b.

6 m

15 m

c.

9 cm

4 cm

d.

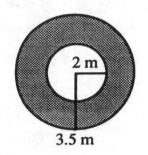

2 m

3.5 m

1.2 Consider an experiment which involves tossing a coin and counting the number of times that it lands heads up. After 65 tosses, you record 31 heads.

    a. What is the experimental probability of the coin landing heads up?

    b. What is the theoretical probability of the coin landing heads up?

1.3 Graph the following inequality on a two-dimensional coordinate system: $x + y \geq 1$.

Activity 2

2.1   Consider an experiment which involves drawing a card out of a standard deck of 52 playing cards. Determine the theoretical probability of drawing each of the following:

  a. a six

  b. a heart

  c. a face card

  d. a club or a diamond.

2.2   Consider an experiment which involves rolling a six-sided die and recording the number that appears.

  a. List all the possible outcomes of this experiment.

  b. What is the theoretical probability of each outcome?

  c. What is the expected value of this experiment?

2.3   Solve each of the following equations for x.

  a. $\dfrac{2}{3}x = 5$

  b. $\dfrac{1}{13}x = 2$

Activity 3

3.1   Consider an experiment in which three cards—an ace, a king and a queen—are placed face down on a table. The cards are then turned over, one at a time.

  a. Draw a tree diagram that shows all the possible sequences in which the cards may be turned over.

  b. How many outcomes are there in the sample space for this experiment?

  c. What is the probability that the ace is the first card turned over?

  d. What is the probability that the queen is the first card and the ace is the second card?

3.2   A bag contains 20 red marbles, 16 green marbles, and 12 blue marbles. Consider an experiment in which two marbles are drawn from the bag, one at a time and without replacement.

  a. What is the probability that the first marble is blue?

  b. What is the probability that the first marble is red?

  c. If the first marble is green, what is the probability that the second marble is red?

Answers to Flashbacks

Activity 1

1.1   **a.** $328/360 \cdot \pi \cdot 5^2 = 205\pi/9 \approx 71.56 \text{ m}^2$

     b. $15 \cdot 6 = 90 \text{ m}^2$

     c. $1/2 \cdot 4 \cdot 9 = 18 \text{ cm}^2$

     d. $(\pi \cdot 3.5^2) - (\pi \cdot 2^2) \approx 25.92 \text{ m}^2$

1.2   **a.** $31/65 \approx 0.48$

     b. $1/2 \approx 0.5$

1.3   Sample graph:

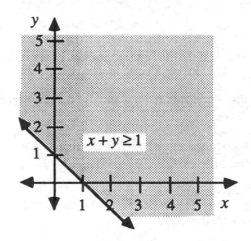

Activity 2

2.1   **a.** $1/13 \approx 0.08$

     b. $1/4 = 0.25$

     c. $3/13 \approx 0.23$

     d. $1/2 = 0.5$

2.2   **a.** There are six possible outcomes: 1, 2, 3, 4, 5, and 6.

     b. The theoretical probability of each outcome is $1/6 \approx 0.17$.

     c. The expected value is:

$$\frac{1}{6} \cdot 1 + \frac{1}{6} \cdot 2 + \frac{1}{6} \cdot 3 + \frac{1}{6} \cdot 4 + \frac{1}{6} \cdot 5 + \frac{1}{6} \cdot 6 = \frac{7}{2}$$

2.3   **a.** $x = 15/2 = 7.5$

       b. $x = 26$

Activity 3

3.1   **a.** Sample tree diagram:

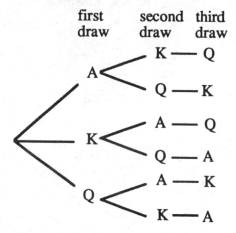

       b. The sample space contains 6 equally likely possibilities: AKQ, AQK, KAQ, KQA, QAK, and QKA.

       c. Since the ace appears first in 2 of the 6 outcomes, the probability is $2/6 \approx 0.33$.

       d. Since the queen appears first and the ace second in 1 of the 6 outcomes, the probability is $1/6 \approx 0.17$.

3.2   **a.** $12/48 = 1/4 = 0.25$

       b. $20/48 = 5/12 \approx 0.42$

       c. $20/47 \approx 0.43$

Atomic Clocks
Are Ticking

You've found the remains of an old cooking fire. How do you tell if that lump of charcoal is 10 years old, or 10,000? In this module, you explore one method that archaeologists use to tell time.

John Freal • Sandy Johnson • Anne Merrifield

Atomic Clocks Are Ticking

Overview

This module uses radioactive decay and carbon dating to develop models of exponential decay and examine negative and fractional exponents. Exponential equations are solved graphically and by guess-and-check using a calculator.

Objectives

In this module, students will:

- develop models of exponential decay
- examine the relationship between negative and positive exponents
- use equations containing negative exponents as mathematical models
- examine the relationship between rational exponents and roots
- develop properties of exponents.

Prerequisites

For this module, students should know:

- how to interpret an exponential expression
- how to model exponential growth using equations of the form $y = a \bullet b^x$
- scientific notation
- how to use a spreadsheet.

Time Line

Activity	1	2	3	Summary Assessment	Total
Days	2	3	3	2	10

Materials Required

Materials	Activity			
	1	2	3	Summary Assessment
chips	X			
graph paper	X		X	
box with lid	X			
dice (optional)			X	

Technology

Software	Activity			
	1	2	3	Summary Assessment
graphing utility	X	X	X	X
spreadsheet	X	X	X	

Atomic Clocks Are Ticking

Introduction (page 271)

The opening narrative introduces students to carbon dating. As the module progresses, students eventually gain a more accurate understanding of radioactive decay. In the summary assessment, students will use Professor Cordova's data to determine the age of charcoal found in the cave.

Note: Students should not perceive radioactive decay as the "death" of an atom. A radioactive atom typically emits a small particle (or particles) from the nucleus—resulting in a new nucleus with a different number of protons. The decay of an atom of carbon-14, for example, produces an atom of nitrogen.

(page 271)

Activity 1

In this activity, students use equations of the form $y = a \cdot b^x$ to model data collected during a simulation of radioactive decay. In this simulation, each shake of the container represents a half-life. **Note:** In Activity **3**, students use a simulation which produces half-life values that are not whole units.

Materials List

- chips (32 per group)
- flat container with lid (one per group)

Teacher Note

To conduct the exploration, each group will require 32 chips (such as poker chips) that can be marked on one side. As an alternative, you may wish to use pennies as chips. Pizza boxes or shoe boxes provide suitable containers.

Technology

- graphing utility
- spreadsheet (optional)

Exploration

Note: Students should save their data for use in the assignment.

a–f.   Students simulate the process of radioactive decay. It should take from 4 to 7 shakes to remove all the chips. Sample data:

Shake	No. of Chips Remaining
0	32
1	15
2	12
3	8
4	3
5	1
6	1
7	0

g.   A graph of the sample data appears below.

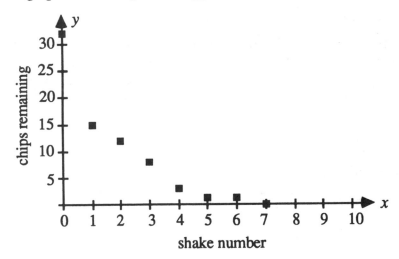

Discussion

a.   Sample response: The number of remaining chips appears to decrease more slowly as the shake number increases.

b.   Answers will vary. Sample response: The general shapes of the graphs are the same, with the number of chips decreasing as the shake number increases. However, different numbers of shakes were required to remove all the chips, and the graphs vary in steepness.

c.   Since the probability of a chip landing with the mark up is 1/2, students should expect half of the chips to be removed and half to remain.

d.   When a positive number is multiplied by a factor between 0 and 1, the number decreases.

e. **1.** Sample response: The value of y represents the worth of the machine at the end of half a year, or 6 months.

    2. Sample response: The value of y represents the worth of the machine at the end of one-third of a year, or 4 months.

f. Answers will vary, depending on the calculator used.

    1. Sample response: Type "0.81^(1/2)" then press the enter button.

    2. Sample response: Type "0.81^(1/3)" then press the enter button.

g. Students should realize that the value of $(0.81)^{1/2}$ is the square root of 0.81, or 0.9.

h. Students should conjecture that since an exponent of 1/2 in the expression $(0.81)^{1/2}$ represents the square root, an exponent of 1/3 in the expression $(0.81)^{1/3}$ represents the cube root of 0.81. This can be verified by cubing the value reported by the calculator for $(0.81)^{1/3}$.

i. **1.** If the equation models exponential growth, $b > 1$.

    2. If the equation models exponential decay, $0 < b < 1$.

Assignment (page 274)

1.1 **a.** 5

    b. 3

    c. 7

    d. 2

1.2 **a.** The table below shows the percent decrease after each shake for the sample data given in the exploration:

Shake	No. of Chips Remaining	Percent Decrease
0	32	
1	15	47%
2	12	20%
3	8	33%
4	3	63%
5	1	67%
6	1	0%
7	0	100%

b. 1. Answers will vary. The mean of the percents of decrease for the sample data shown above is 47%.

2. Sample response: I would expect the mean of the percents of decrease to be close to 50%, because each chip has a 50% chance of having its mark showing.

c. Sample response: The mean of the percents of decrease can be used as the rate of decay, which is also a percentage, because they measure the same thing.

d. Answers will vary. For the sample data, the rate of decay is –0.47. In this case, $b = 1 - 0.47 = 0.53$.

e. Since the initial population is 32, the equation that models the data is $y = 32 \cdot (0.53)^x$.

1.3 A completed table is shown below.

	Initial Population	Rate of Growth or Decay	Model Equation of the Form $y = a \cdot b^x$
a.	500	8%	$y = 500 \cdot (1.08)^x$
b.	20,000	–11%	$y = 20{,}000 \cdot (0.89)^x$
c.	100	–32%	$y = 100 \cdot (0.68)^x$

1.4 $5.02 \cdot 10^{22} / 1 \cdot 10^{12} \approx 5 \cdot 10^{10}$ atoms

1.5 Using an equation of the form $y = a \cdot b^x$, the initial population a is $4 \cdot 10^{14}$ chips, b is 0.5, and the number of shakes x is 3. Solving for y gives $5 \cdot 10^{13}$ or 50 trillion chips.

Students also may solve this problem as follows: After the first shake, the number of chips is $(4 \cdot 10^{14})/2 = 2 \cdot 10^{14}$; after the second shake, the number of chips is $(2 \cdot 10^{14})/2 = 1 \cdot 10^{14}$; after the third shake, the number of chips is $(1 \cdot 10^{14})/2 = 5 \cdot 10^{13}$.

1.6 Sample response: To find the number of atoms in the previous year, multiply by 2: $3.8 \cdot 10^{13}(2) = 7.6 \cdot 10^{13}$ atoms. **Note:** Some students may substitute –1 for x in the equation $y = (3.8 \cdot 10^{13})(0.5^x)$ to calculate an answer. Negative exponents are introduced in Activity **2**.

1.7 Sample response: Starting with $1 \cdot 10^{12}$ and repeatedly multiplying by 0.5 for each decade, it would take 10 decades before the number of atoms was less than $1 \cdot 10^9$ (one billion).

*1.8   **a.** Since $b > 1$, this equation models exponential growth. In this case, $1.055 = 1 + r$ or $r = 0.055$. As x increases, the graph increases gradually at first, then dramatically.

   b. Since $0 < b < 1$, this equation models exponential decay. In this case, $0.50 = 1 + r$ or $r = -0.50$. As x increases, the graph decreases dramatically at first, then gradually.

   c. Since $0 < b < 1$, this equation models exponential decay. In this case, $0.75 = 1 + r$ or $r = -0.25$. As x increases, the graph decreases dramatically at first, then gradually.

* * * * *

1.9   **a.** The total amount of money in the account after x years may be modeled by the equation $y = 1000 \cdot (1 + 0.08)^x = 1000 \cdot (1.08)^x$.

   b. The account balance after 5 years is $y = 1000 \cdot (1.08)^5 = \$1469.33$.

   c. **1.** Sample graph:

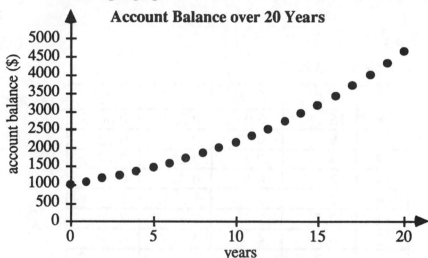

Account Balance over 20 Years

   2. The account balance will reach \$2000 in about 9 years.

   d. Answers may vary. For a 16-year-old student, the account balance may be calculated as follows: $y = 1000 \cdot (1.08)^{49} \approx \$43,427.42$.

1.10   **a.** The town's initial population was 50,000.

   b. The population decreased to 25,000 between year 6 and year 7.

   c. The population at year 15 is about 11,000.

   d. Answers may vary slightly. The rate of decrease is 10% per year.

   e. **1.** Sample response: $y = 50,000 \cdot (0.90)^x$.

   2. The estimated value from the graph and the approximate value from the equation should be reasonably close. Using the sample equation given above, $y = 50,000 \cdot (0.90)^{15} \approx 10,295$.

* * * * * * * * *

351

Activity 2

In this activity, students use negative values for x in equations of the form $y = a \cdot b^x$ to represent periods of time before the present. This allows them to explore negative exponents and continue their investigation of carbon dating.

Materials List

- none

Technology

- spreadsheet
- graphing utility

Exploration 1

(page 277)

a.   Sample spreadsheet:

x	2^x	$(1/2)^x$	$1/2^x$	2^{-x}
4	16	0.0625	0.0625	0.0625
3	8	0.125	0.125	0.125
2	4	0.25	0.25	0.25
1	2	0.5	0.5	0.5
0	1	1	1	1
−1	0.5	2	2	2
−2	0.25	4	4	4
−3	0.125	8	8	8
−4	0.0625	16	16	16

b.   Sample response: The entries in the $(1/2)^x$, $1/2^x$, and 2^{-x} columns are the same. Since $1/2^x$ is the reciprocal of 2^x, then $(1/2)^x$ and 2^{-x} are also reciprocals of 2^x.

c.   Sample graph:

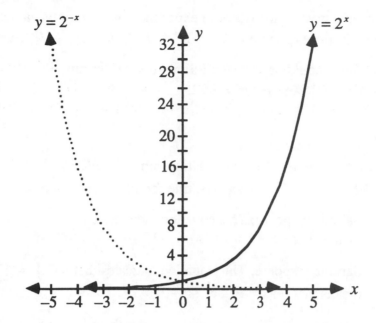

$y = 2^{-x}$ $y = 2^{x}$

Discussion

(page 277)

a. $2^{0} = 1$

b.   The expressions $(1/2)^{x}$, $1/2^{x}$, and 2^{-x} are equal.

c.   Sample response: The value of 2^{x} is the reciprocal of the value of each of the other expressions.

d.   Sample response: There is no conflict. Because $1^{x} = 1$ for any value of x, $(1/2)^{x} = 1^{x}/2^{x} = 1/2^{x}$.

e.   Sample response:

$$2^{-3} = \frac{1}{2^{3}} = \left(\frac{1}{2}\right)^{3} = \frac{1}{8} = 0.125$$

f.   Sample response: The graphs are reflections of each other in the y-axis.

g.   **1.** Using negative exponents, 2^{3} can be expressed as $(1/2)^{-3}$ or $1/2^{-3}$.

         2. Using negative exponents, $a \cdot b^{2}$ can be expressed as $a \cdot (1/b)^{-2}$, $a \cdot 1/b^{-2}$, or a/b^{-2}.

h.   **1.** Without using negative exponents, 2^{-3} can be expressed as $(1/2)^{3}$ or $1/2^{3}$.

         2. Without using negative exponents, $a \cdot b^{-2}$ can be expressed as $a \cdot (1/b)^{2}$, $a \cdot 1/b^{2}$, or a/b^{2}.

353

Exploration 2 (page 278)

a–c. Students use a spreadsheet to experiment with various values for b, x, and y in the expressions b^{x+y}, b^{x-y}, $b^{x \cdot y}$, $b^x \cdot b^y$, b^x/b^y, and $(b^x)^y$.

They should observe the following relationships: $b^x \cdot b^y = b^{x+y}$, $(b^x)^y = b^{x \cdot y}$, and $b^x/b^y = b^{x-y}$.

Discussion 2 (page 279)

a. Sample response: Yes, the relationships $b^x \cdot b^y = b^{x+y}$, $(b^x)^y = b^{x \cdot y}$, and $b^x/b^y = b^{x-y}$ appear to be true for all values tested.

b.   **1.** Sample response: This equation indicates that $4^{-5} \cdot 4^x = 4^{-5+x}$. This means that $-5 + x = 10$, so $x = 15$.

   2. Sample response: This equation indicates that $\left(4^{-5}\right)^x = 4^{-5x}$. This means that $-5x = 10$ so $x = -2$.

c. Sample response: This equation indicates that $\left(5^3\right)^x = 5^{3 \cdot x}$. This means that $3x = 1$ so $x = 1/3$.

d.   **1.** $16^{0.25} = 16^{25/100} = 16^{1/4} = \sqrt[4]{16} = 2$

   2. $16^{3/4} = \left(\sqrt[4]{16}\right)^3 = \sqrt[4]{4096} = 8$

e. Sample response: In this case, 4.3 represents the number of units of time that have passed since the initial level of radioactivity was measured.

f. Sample responses:

$$b^{4.3} = b^4 \cdot b^{0.3} = b^4 \cdot b^{3/10} = b^4 \cdot \left(\sqrt[10]{b}\right)^3 \text{ or } b^{4.3} = b^{43/10} = \left(\sqrt[10]{b}\right)^{43}$$

g.   **1.** Sample response:

$(-8)^{2/6} = \sqrt[6]{-8^2} = \sqrt[6]{64} = 2$ $(-8)^{1/3} = \sqrt[3]{-8^1} = -2$

$(-8)^{2/6} = \left(\sqrt[6]{-8}\right)^2 = \text{ undefined}$ $(-8)^{1/3} = \left(\sqrt[3]{-8}\right)^1 = -2$

$(-8)^{2/6} = \left(-8^2\right)^{1/6} = 2$ $(-8)^{1/3} = \left(-8^1\right)^{1/3} = -2$

$(-8)^{2/6} = \left(-8^{1/6}\right)^2 = \text{ undefined}$ $(-8)^{1/3} = \left(-8^{1/3}\right)^1 = -2$

Note: Some forms of technology may give results that are inconsistent with this sample response. For example, some calculators may report that $(-8)^{2/6} = -2$.

354

2. Sample response: When the rational exponent is not in lowest terms, raising a base to that power may be undefined or may give conflicting values. **Note:** Another way of approaching this topic is to consider the rational exponent as a decimal. This works well when the decimal is terminating. If the decimal is non-terminating, however, one must consider the corresponding limit.

Assignment

(page 280)

2.1   **a. 1.** In 2 years, 1/4 of the radioactive atoms will remain.

          2. Since $x = 0$ indicates that no time has passed, the number of atoms would remain the same.

          3. Two years earlier, the number of radioactive atoms was four times the present number.

       b. Sample response: The –2 indicates that you are calculating the number of atoms that were present two years earlier.

2.2   **a.** Sample response: This represents the number of bacteria present after 4 min.

       b. Sample response: This represents the number of bacteria present 4 min before the initial population was counted.

       c. The expression can be rewritten as $32 \cdot \left(1/2^4\right)$ or $32 \cdot (1/2)^4$.

2.3   **a.** Sample response: $y = 32 \cdot 2^{-x}$.

       b. Some students may solve this problem by graphing $y = 32 \cdot (1/2)^x$ and using the trace feature on their graphing utility. Some may write 32 as 2^5 and use the properties of exponents; others may choose to use a spreadsheet.

          1. 2 shakes

          2. 4 shakes

          3. –1 shakes

          4. –2 shakes

          5. 0 shakes

2.4   Sample response:

$$\left(\frac{a}{b}\right)^{-x} = \frac{a^{-x}}{b^{-x}} = \frac{1/a^x}{1/b^x} = \frac{b^x}{a^x} = \left(\frac{b}{a}\right)^x$$

2.5   **a.** 3^{-3}

    b. a^{-b}

    c. $\dfrac{3^2}{5^2} = \dfrac{9}{25}$

    d. $(5/3)^{-2}$

    e. $(3/4)^2$

*2.6   **a.** Using $5.12 \bullet 10^{14}$ for a and $(1-0.5)$ for b, the equation is:
$3.2 \bullet 10^{13} = 5.12 \bullet 10^{14} \bullet (0.5)^x$.

    b. Sample response: The equation $3.2 \bullet 10^{13} = 5.12 \bullet 10^{14} \bullet (0.5)^x$ can be simplified to $0.0625 = (0.5)^x$, or $1/16 = (1/2)^x$. In this case, $x = 4$. The radioactive atoms in the artifact began decaying 4 intervals of time ago.

2.7   **a.** Sample response: Changing the initial population changes the value of a, which in turn changes the y-intercept. The graph appears less steep as the value of a approaches 0. **Note:** Although the graph no longer models decay, it curves downward when the value of a becomes negative and appears steeper as a continues to decrease. When $a = 0$, the graph of $y = a \bullet b^x$ is the horizontal line $y = 0$.

    b. Sample response: Since $b = 1 + r$, changing the rate of decay changes b. For values of b between 0 and 1, the graph becomes less steep for values closer to 0. When b is 0, the graph coincides with the x-axis. When b is 1, the curve coincides with the line $y = a$. **Note:** Although the graph no longer models decay, it curves upward and to the right instead of upward and to the left for values of b greater than 1. When b is less than 0, the graph alternates between positive and negative values.

*2.8   Sample response: The equation indicates that the initial number of radioactive atoms in the object was 4000. The rate of decay is $-3/20$. This means that 15% of the radioactive material decays in each time interval.

2.9   **a.** $\left(x^3\right)^{1/3} = x^{3 \bullet 1/3} = x^1 = x$

    b. $x = 4$

2.10 **a.** Sample response: In this case, $x = 3$. This can be found by raising both sides of the equation to a power of 1/6.

$$\left(x^6\right)^{1/6} = 729^{1/6}$$
$$x^{6 \cdot 1/6} = 729^{1/6}$$
$$x = 729^{1/6} = 3$$

b. Sample response: In this case, $x = 256$. This can be found by raising both sides of the equation to the 8th power.

$$x^{0.125} = 2$$
$$x^{1/8} = 2$$
$$\left(x^{1/8}\right)^8 = 2^8$$
$$x = 256$$

b. Sample response:

$$10^5 \cdot x = 10^{16}$$
$$x = 10^{16}/10^5$$
$$= 10^{16-5} = 10^{11}$$

2.11 **a.** Since $b = 2$, $r = 1$. Because r is positive, this equation models a pattern of exponential growth.

b. Since $b \approx 1.1$, $r \approx 0.1$. Because r is positive, this equation models a pattern of exponential growth.

c. Since $b \approx 0.5$, $r \approx -0.5$. Because r is negative, this equation models a pattern of exponential decay.

d. Since $b \approx 0.8$, $r \approx -0.2$. Because r is negative, this equation models a pattern of exponential decay.

$$* \; * \; * \; * \; *$$

2.12 **a.** Sample scatterplot:

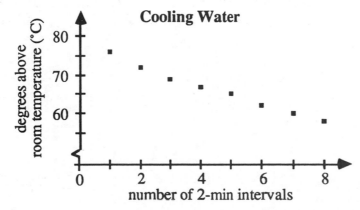

357

b. The mean of the percents of decrease in temperature is approximately 4.1% per 2-min interval.

2-min Interval	Degrees above Room Temperature (°C)	Percent Decrease
1	74	
2	70	5.1%
3	67	4.4%
4	65	3.1%
5	63	3.2%
6	60	5.0%
7	58	3.4%
8	56	3.6%

c. Using the rate of decay from Part **b**, one equation that could be used to model the data is $y = 77(0.959)^x$, where x represents the number of 2-min intervals. Students may find the value of a in their models by trial and error or by examining residuals for various values. **Note:** The regression equation for the data is $y \approx 76(0.962)^x$.

d. Using their model from Part **c**, students can estimate the room temperature by subtracting the value of the function at $x = 0$ from 100° C. Using the equation $y = 77(0.959)^x$, the approximate room temperature is 23° C.

e. Sample response: The exponential equation would not be a good model to predict temperatures before the water is poured because the function increases without bound as x decreases. This would indicate that the water continually increases in temperature as the time prior to pouring the liquid increases.

2.13 The equation $y = 5 \cdot (1 - 0.5)^3$ is equivalent to $y = 5 \cdot (2)^{-3}$. The equation $y = 5 \cdot (2)^3$ is equivalent to $y = 5 \cdot (1/2)^{-3}$. The equation $y = 5 \cdot (2)^{1/3}$ is equivalent to $y = 5 \cdot (0.5)^{-1/3}$.

* * * * * * * * * *

Activity 3

This activity focuses on solving equations of the form $y = a \cdot b^x$ for x.

Materials List

- graph paper
- numbered dice (or other random number generator; one per group)

Technology

- graphing utility
- spreadsheet (optional)

Exploration

a–c.   The simulation requires students to use an appropriate random number generator. It should take about four rounds to reach the first half-life. Although students may need more than 10 rounds to remove all the atoms, 10 is sufficient to show the existing patterns. Sample data:

Round	Number of Radioactive Atoms
0	32
1	29
2	25
3	19
4	16
5	15
6	12
7	10
8	9
9	8
10	6

d.   A graph of the sample data appears in Part e below.

e. **1.** $y = 32 \cdot (5/6)^x$

   2. Sample graph:

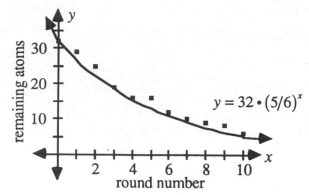

f. **1.** Sample response: The half-life is about 4 rounds.

   2. Using $y = 32 \cdot (5/6)^x$, the half-life is approximately 3.8 rounds.

Discussion

(page 285)

a. Sample response: Since the probability of decay in the simulation is 1/6, about 5/6 of the atoms should remain after each round.

b. The half-life in this exploration is about 4 rounds while the half-life for the simulation in Activity **1** was 1 round (or shake).

c. **1.** Since $a = 32$ and $b = 1 - (1/6) = 5/6$, an appropriate model is $y = 32(5/6)^x$.

   2. Sample response: The value of a in both simulations is 32. The value of b in Activity **3** is 5/6; it was 1/2 in Activity **1**. The value of r in Activity **3** is $-1/6$; it was $-1/2$ in Activity **1**.

Assignment

(page 285)

3.1 **a.** $y = 1.05 \cdot 10^{11} \cdot (0.99997)^x$

   b. The sample is about 51,000 years old. To find a solution, students may graph the equation or use a guess-and-check method. Sample graph:

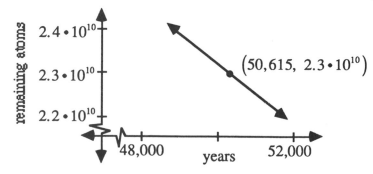

360

3.2 **a.** **1.** $x = 2$

           2. $x = 3$

     b. Sample response: The value of x must be between 2 and 3.

     c. $x \approx 2.52$

     d. $x \approx 3.27$

3.3 The half-life is approximately 3.80 rounds.

3.4 **a.** In all three cases, the problem can be solved by substituting $a/2$ for y. The value of x can then be found by guess-and-check using a calculator. Students also may graph each equation, trace until the y-value equals $a/2$, then record the corresponding x-value. (Students are not expected to use logarithms.)

       In each case, the half-life is about 1.4 time intervals.

     b. Sample response: Since all three equations have the same value for b, they must also have the same rate of decay. Since the half-life is the same in all three cases, the initial number of radioactive atoms does not appear to affect the half-life.

*3.5 **Note:** Radioactive tracers are useful in a number of applications, including engineering, biochemistry, and medicine. Iodine-131 and technetium-99m are two radioactive isotopes used in nuclear medicine. You may wish to consult a local hospital for more details about the use of radioactive tracers.

     a. $y = 100 \cdot 0.8^x$

     b. Sample graph:

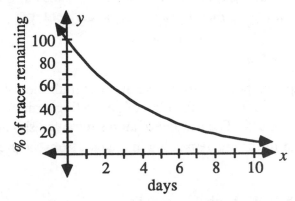

     c. The half-life occurs when $y = 50\%$. From the graph, this takes place after about 3 days.

     d. Sample response: Using the equation $y = 100 \cdot (0.8)^x$ and an exponent of -2, the newly manufactured sample's radioactivity was about 156% of the sample that Kim received.

3.6   **a.** $b = 0.5^{1/12.5} \approx 0.946$; $r \approx -5.39\%$/hour

        b. $b = 0.5^{1/57.8} \approx 0.988$; $r \approx -1.20\%$/century

*3.7   **a.** $b^5 = 0.50$; $b \approx 0.87$

        b. $r \approx -0.13 \approx -13\%$/year

        c. Substituting 0.87 for b and 93 for y in the comparative equation $y = 100b^x$ gives $93 = 100(0.87)^x$. Solving this equation for x, the sample is about 0.5 years old.

*3.8   **a.** The percentage of radioactivity remaining after each hour is equal to the value of b in the equation $50 = 100 \bullet (b)^6$. Solving this equation for b gives $b \approx 0.89$.

        b. $y \approx 100(0.89)^x$

        c. Since 45 min equals 0.75 hours, students should write the equation $y = 100(0.89)^{0.75}$. This yields a value of approximately 92% for y.

        d. After about 20 hours, 10% of the tracer will remain. This can be calculated by solving the equation $10 = 100(0.89)^x$ for x.

        e. The time 3 hours prior to the injection may be represented by $x = -3$. Solving the equation $y = 100(0.89)^{-3}$ for y yields approximately 142. This means that the tracer was 42% more radioactive at the time of manufacture.

3.9   Sample response: Since 5730 years is 57.3 centuries, the comparative equation $50 = 100(b)^{57.3}$ can be used to find the rate of decay in centuries. Solving for b yields $b = 0.5^{1/57.3} \approx 0.988$. Since $b = 1 + r$, the rate of decay is about −0.012 or −1.2% per century.

* * * * *

3.10 $x = 0.25$ or $1/4$

3.11   **a.** Sample response: Since there are four multiples of 5 in the numbers from 1 to 20, the probability of generating a multiple of 5 is 4/20 or 1/5. The number of atoms removed should be approximately 1/5 of the atoms remaining in the box from the previous round.

        b. 4/5

        c. The half-life is about 3 rounds.

        d. $y = 32 \bullet (0.8)^x$

3.12   **a.** Approximately 97.6% of the initial radioactivity remains after 1 year. This can be calculated by finding the value of b using the known half-life of strontium-90:

$$50 = 100 \cdot (b)^{28}$$
$$0.5^{1/28} = b$$
$$0.976 \approx b$$

b. Solving the equation $1 = 100(0.976)^x$ for x, it will take about 190 years for the level of radioactivity to drop below 1%.

c. Solving the equation $y = 100(0.976)^{-5}$ for y yields about 113. This means that the material was approximately 13% more radioactive 5 years ago.

d. **Note:** The labels on the x-axis in the following sample response were generated by adding the year 1993 to the value of x. Students should add the present year to x.

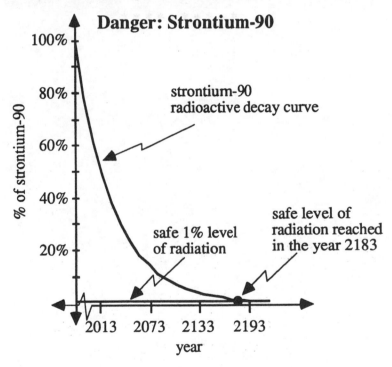

363

3.13   a. To find the growth rate, students should solve the following
            equation for b:

$$0.65 = 0.25 \cdot b^{24}$$
$$b = \sqrt[24]{2.6}$$
$$b \approx 1.04$$
$$r \approx 4\%$$

        b. The following sample equation models the price of the candy bar
            where x represents the number of years after 1972:

$$y = 0.25 \cdot (1.04)^x$$

        c. Solving the equation $0.10 = 0.25 \cdot (1.04)^x$ for x yields
            approximately -23.4. This corresponds with the year 1948.

        d. Solving the equation $1.00 = 0.25 \cdot (1.04)^x$ for x yields
            approximately 35.3. This corresponds with the year 2008.

* * * * * * * * * *

Answers to Summary Assessment (page 289)

1. Students can solve this problem efficiently by using the trace function on a graphing calculator. Professor Cordova's maximum estimate of 12,000 years (120 centuries) should give students an idea of the appropriate domain. Using the value of b found in Problem **4.7**, students may use the equation $y = 100(0.988)^x$.

Layer	% C-14 Activity	Age (in centuries)
1	91.6	7.3
2	83.3	15.1
3	81.6	16.8
4	78.5	20.0
5	75.0	23.8
6	71.2	28.1
7	65.4	35.2
8	47.4	61.8
9	42.9	70.1
10	39.9	76.1
11	32.1	94.1

2. Because 11,500 years is about two half-lives ago, about 25% of the original carbon-14 should remain. This solution can also be found by substituting 115 for x in the equation $y = 100(0.988)^x$.

3. a. Using the comparative equation $y = 100b^x$ and the value of b for carbon-14 found in Problem **4.7**, $112 = 100(0.988)^x$. Solving for x, $x \approx -9.4$ centuries. The negative sign indicates that the carbon-14 in the innermost ring has been decaying 940 years longer than the carbon-14 in the outermost ring.

   b. The age of the tree using carbon dating is the same as the age determined by counting the rings.

1. The following graph shows the change in radioactivity for a substance over time. Use the graph to estimate the half-life of the substance.

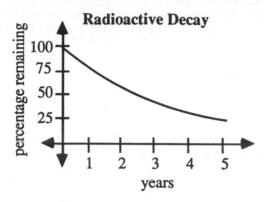

2. Give an example of a function of the form $y = a \cdot b^x$ that models each of the following situations and explain why your example is appropriate:

    a. exponential growth

    b. exponential decay.

3. Find the value of x, to the nearest integer, in each of the following equations:

    a. $48 = 24(0.5)^x$

    b. $1/2 = (4/5)^x$

4. Former U.S. President George Bush was successfully treated for thyroid disease with a radioactive form of iodine. When the thyroid gland absorbs a dose of iodine-131, the process of radioactive decay kills the diseased cells.

    a. Iodine-131 has a half-life of 8 days. What percentage of radioactivity in a dose of iodine-131 remains after 1 day? Explain your response.

    b. Write an equation of the form $y = 100b^x$ that models the decay of iodine-131.

    c. Graph the decay of a dose of iodine-131 over 3 weeks.

    d. What percentage of radioactivity in a dose of iodine-131 remains after 1 week?

    e. Iodine therapy can lose its effectiveness when the level of radioactivity in a dose falls below 20%. After how many days does this occur? Explain your response.

Answers to Module Assessment

1. The half-life is about 2.5 years.

2. a. Sample response: In exponential growth, the rate is positive. Since $b = 1 + r$, the value for b must be greater than 1. One possible equation is $y = 100 \cdot 2^x$.

    b. Sample response: In exponential decay, the rate is negative, so the value of b must be less than 1 (but greater than 0). One possible equation is $y = 100(0.5)^x$.

3. a. $x = -1$

    b. $x \approx 3$

4. a. Solving the equation $50 = 100b^8$ for b gives $b \approx 0.917$. The percentage of radioactivity remaining after 1 day is about 91.7%.

    b. $y = 100(0.917)^x$

    c. Sample response:

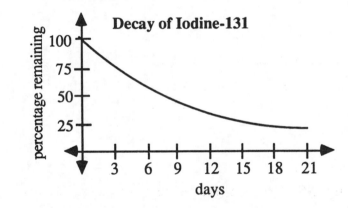

    d. $100(0.917)^7 \approx 54.5\%$

    e. Using the trace function on a graphing calculator, the graph of $y = 100(0.917)^x$ drops below the line $y = 20$ between the 18th and 19th day.

Selected References

Libby, W. F. *Radiocarbon Dating*. Chicago, IL: University of Chicago Press, 1952.

Taylor, R. E. *Radiocarbon Dating: An Archaeological Perspective*. Orlando, FL: Academic Press, 1987

Flashbacks

Activity 1

1.1   When flipping a fair coin, what is the probability of getting tails?

1.2   Simplify each of the following expressions.

    a. $\left(6.33 \cdot 10^4\right)/\left(5 \cdot 10^2\right)$

    b. $\left(4.18 \cdot 10^{13}\right) \cdot 2$

1.3   Express each of the following numbers as a power of 10.

    a. one hundred

    b. one million

    c. one

Activity 2

2.1   Solve for x in each equation below.

    a. $3 \cdot x = 1$

    b. $2 \cdot x = 1$

2.2   Simplify each of the following expressions.

    a. 2^3

    b. $\left(1/2\right)^3$

    c. $1/2^3$

2.3   Find the value of x in each of the following equations.

    a. $2^x = 4$

    b. $3^x = 27$

    c. $0.5^x = 0.0625$

2.4   The equation $y = 5 \cdot 2^x$ models the annual growth in a population. In this model, describe what is represented by each of the following:

    a. y

    b. 5

    c. 2

    d. x

Activity 3

3.1   A jar contains 200 jelly beans. Write an equation that describes the number of jelly beans remaining in the jar for each of the following situations:

  a. 1/3 of the jelly beans are removed each minute

  b. 20% of the jelly beans are removed each minute

  c. 60% of the jelly beans are removed each minute.

3.2   Write each of the following in the form a/b where a and b are integers:

  a. 2^{-2}

  b. 3^{-3}

  c. 0.6^{-2}

3.3   **a.** Graph the equation $y = 2000(0.35)^x$.

  b. Find the value of x when y is 100.

Answers to Flashbacks

Activity 1

1.1   50%

1.2   **a.** $1.266 \cdot 10^2$

         b. $8.36 \cdot 10^{13}$

1.3   **a.** 10^2

         b. 10^6

         c. 10^0

Activity 2

2.1   **a.** $x = 1/3$

         b. $x = 1/2$

2.2   **a.** 8

         b. 1/8

         c. 1/8

2.3   **a.** $x = 2$

         b. $x = 3$

         c. $x = 4$

2.4   **a.** The variable y represents the population after x years.

         b. The quantity 5 represents the initial population.

         c. The quantity 2 represents $1 + r$, where r is the growth rate.

         d. The variable x represents the time in years.

Activity 3

3.1   **a.** $y = 200 \cdot (2/3)^x$

  b. $y = 200 \cdot (0.8)^x$

  c. $y = 200 \cdot (0.4)^x$

3.2   **a.** 1/4

  b. 1/27

  c. 25/9

3.3   **a.** Sample graph:

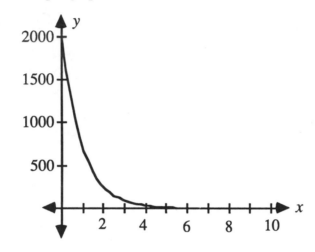

  b. When $y = 100$, $x \approx 2.85$.